DICTIONARY of MECHANICS

A handbook for teachers and students

by

Janet Jagger
(The Mathematical Association)

in collaboration with

Simon Carson
(The Institute of Physics)

This dictionary will be useful for

- post GCSE mathematics and physics students in schools and colleges
- mathematics and physics teachers in schools
- first year undergraduate mathematics and physics students
- PGCE students of mathematics and physics

ISBN 0 906588 46 4

The dictionary can be obtained from:

The Mathematical Association
259 London Road
Leicester
LE2 3BE
0116 221 0013
www.m-a.org.uk

The Institute of Physics
76 Portland Place
London
0207 4704800

PREFACE

This is the second edition of this dictionary, the first one having been published in 1990 as part of the Mechanics-in-Action Project. This dictionary provides definitions and explanations of the concepts and terms found in most first courses in Newtonian mechanics.

Some definitions are grouped together, e.g. mass and weight, so that their meanings can be compared and contrasted in order to give the reader a fuller picture; in this respect, the book is more a handbook than a dictionary.

As students progress through their course, they start with a restricted form of the definition of a term; this is refined or subtly changed at a later stage in their studies. Thus where appropriate, a definition is first given in its elementary form, and then the more advanced form is introduced; for instance 'work done by a force' is first defined as force times distance and finally as the line integral. In this way, I hope that students will be able to access the knowledge that they require at whatever stage they happen to be. Some of the standard letters for quantities are used without definition – please consult the list of notation and abbreviations on the next page.

I wish to thank Dr E A B Cole of Leeds Univesity for his help with some of the words connected with his own subject of relativity. I am also indebted to Dr Simon Carson of the Institute of Physics who read this dictionary with great care and who made many helpful suggestions. Thanks also to Tom Roper and Bill Richardson for their work in reading through and in formatting the text.

Dr J M Jagger

Easter 2000

Distribution address:–

The Mathematical Association, 259, London Road, Leicester, LE2 3BE

NOTATION AND ABBREVIATIONS

r	distance from origin
$\mathbf{r}$	position vector
$A(\mathbf{r})$	point A whose position vector is $\mathbf{r}$
v, $\mathbf{v}$	speed, velocity at time t
u, $\mathbf{u}$	initial speed, initial velocity
a	acceleration at time t
$\dot{\mathbf{r}}$, $\ddot{\mathbf{r}}$	velocity, acceleration at time t
g	magnitude of the acceleration due to gravity ($9{\cdot}8\ \mathrm{ms}^{-2}$)
ω, $\boldsymbol{\omega}$	angular speed, angular velocity
m, M	mass
I	moment of inertia

LHS, RHS — left hand side, right hand side (of an equation)

A bold letter is used to indicate a vector quantity and an italic for a scalar quantity.

The multiplication sign '×' is used to indicate the ordinary product of two numbers as well as the vector product of two vectors. To ensure that there is no confusion, I have indicated a vector product by the words 'vector product', except in a very few instances where the meaning of the symbol is obvious.

The following arrow conventions are observed:–

velocity	⟶
acceleration	⟶⟶ (double-headed arrow)
force	⟶▷ (open-headed arrow)

A

ACCELERATION In common usage, this is a measure of how fast a speed is increasing, but mathematically acceleration is defined as the rate of change of velocity. It is a vector quantity; the SI unit is ms^{-2}.

Thus acceleration $= \dfrac{d\mathbf{v}}{dt} = \dfrac{d\ \mathbf{r}}{dt^2}$.

(1) If a velocity $\mathbf{u}$ becomes a velocity $\mathbf{v}$ in time t, then the average acceleration $= \dfrac{\mathbf{v} - \mathbf{u}}{t}$ (N.B. **vector** subtraction).

(2) The acceleration of a particle P moving with constant speed v in a circle with centre O and radius r has magnitude v^2 / r or $r\omega^2$ and it is in the direction $\overrightarrow{PO}$.

From the definition, it will be noted that a body is accelerating if the velocity changes because of a direction change, even if the speed is constant. For instance, if a particle is travelling in a horizontal circle with constant speed, the velocity is changing at every instant because of the varying direction of motion and so the particle must have an acceleration. This aspect of acceleration – constant speed round a curve – is a notion that contradicts the everyday meaning of acceleration and can be a source of confusion. It arises from the mathematics because velocity is a vector quantity and acceleration the rate of change of this vector.

For more advanced work, you may need (3) and (4):–

(3) The acceleration of a particle, moving in a plane, whose polar coordinates are (r, θ) is given by

$$\ddot{\mathbf{r}} = \left(\ddot{r} - r\dot{\theta}^2\right)\hat{\mathbf{r}} + \left(r\ddot{\theta} + 2\dot{r}\dot{\theta}\right)\hat{\boldsymbol{\theta}}$$

where $\hat{\mathbf{r}}$ is the unit vector parallel to the position vector and $\hat{\boldsymbol{\theta}}$ is the unit vector perpendicular to $\hat{\mathbf{r}}$ in the direction of increasing θ.

(4) In general, for a particle P moving along any curve with speed v, the acceleration consists of two components:

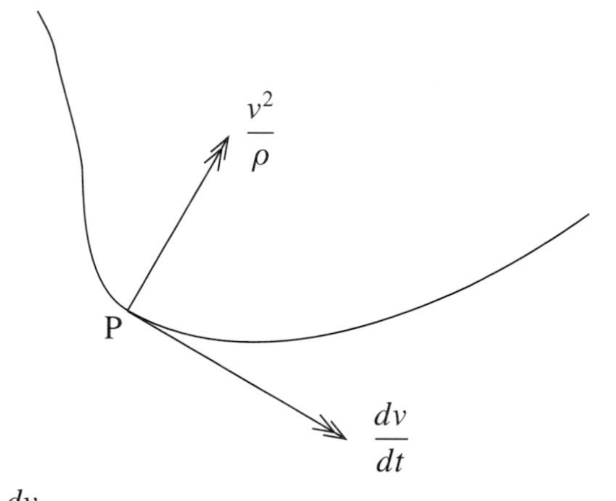

a) $\frac{dv}{dt}$ directed along the tangent to the curve.
This is the everyday meaning of acceleration.

b) $\frac{v^2}{\rho}$ at right angles to the tangent to the curve at P and directed towards the centre of curvature of the curve.
(ρ is the radius of curvature of the curve at P).

The resultant acceleration of P is the vector sum of the two components.

N.B. The acceleration $\frac{dv}{dt}$ (i.e. rate of change of speed) is not the magnitude of the vector acceleration, but only the magnitude of one component.

AMPLITUDE See ***Simple Harmonic Motion***.

ANGULAR ACCELERATION Rate of change of angular velocity.

ANGULAR MOMENTUM

(1) For a particle, angular momentum, or 'moment of momentum', about a point O is defined as the vector product $\mathbf{r} \times m\mathbf{v}$ where $\mathbf{r}$ is the position vector of the particle relative to O (cf. moment of a force).

(2) For a rigid body, rotating about a fixed axis, its angular momentum about the axis is $I\omega$ where I is the moment of inertia of the body about the axis.

The SI unit of angular momentum is kg m^2 s^{-1}.

For a rigid body, angular momentum is analogous to linear momentum for the following reasons; firstly their formulae $I\omega$ and $m\mathbf{v}$ (where $\mathbf{v}$ is the velocity of the centre of gravity of the rigid body) are similar. And secondly, the fundamental equations which govern the motion of a rigid body indicate the physical similarities of the two concepts:–

(A) sum of the external forces = rate of change of linear momentum

(B) sum of the moments of the external forces
= rate of change of angular momentum
(relative to any fixed point or to the centre of mass of the body).

Thus linear momentum is a measure of how hard it is to bring the centre of mass of a body to rest – this depends on the mass and the (linear) velocity of the body. Whereas angular momentum is a measure of how hard it is to stop it rotating – this depends on the moment of inertia and the angular velocity.

See also ***Moment of Inertia***.

ANGULAR SPEED Consider a point P moving in a plane in which O is a fixed point and OA a fixed direction.

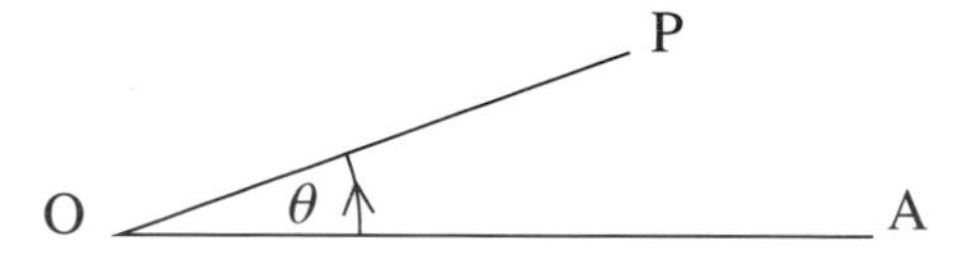

Then as P moves, the angle θ will change. The angular speed of OP is the rate of change of θ with respect to time, written $\frac{d\theta}{dt}$ or $\dot{\theta}$.

The units are usually radians per second but could also be, for instance, revolutions per minute. The angular speed of the line OP is sometimes referred to as the 'angular speed of the point P about O' but, strictly, it is a property of the line OP rather than the point P.

The symbol ω is often used to denote angular speed.

For circular motion, the linear speed is related to the angular speed by the formula $v = r\omega$.

ANGULAR VELOCITY The vector whose magnitude is the angular speed as defined above and whose direction is parallel to the axis of rotation; in the diagram for angular speed, the angular velocity of P is perpendicular to OAP and coming up out of the plane of the paper. Angular velocity is usually denoted by the symbol $\boldsymbol{\omega}$.

For motion in a plane, angular speed is often referred to as angular velocity even though no direction is included in the scalar symbols $\dot{\theta}$ or ω. But for the motion of a rigid body in general, where the axis of rotation may vary, the direction of the angular velocity is as important as its magnitude.

To obtain the equation connecting angular velocity and linear velocity, suppose P is a point of a rigid body which is rotating about a fixed axis ON as shown in the diagram.

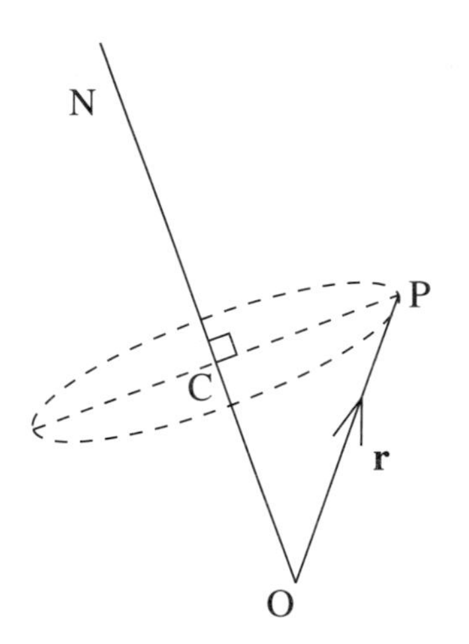

The angular velocity $\boldsymbol{\omega}$ is parallel to $\overrightarrow{ON}$.
$|\boldsymbol{\omega}|$ is the angular speed of P about the axis ON.
$\angle$ PCO is a right angle.

If the axis is fixed, P will describe a circle about C on ON, and its velocity v is given by the vector product

$$\mathbf{v} = \boldsymbol{\omega} \times \mathbf{r} \qquad (\text{where } \overrightarrow{OP} = \mathbf{r}).$$

This can be checked out using the definition of a vector product.

viz. (a) the direction of **v** is at right angles to both ON and OP and into the page, according to the right-hand screw rule,

and (b) the magnitude of the velocity
$= |\mathbf{v}| = |\boldsymbol{\omega} \times \mathbf{r}| = \omega \times OP \times \sin \angle POC = \omega \times CP$
i.e. $v = \text{radius} \times \omega$ as expected.

Even if the axis is not fixed, the same formula for **v** holds for the velocity of P relative to the point O on the axis.

See also ***Vector product***.

AVERAGE SPEED Total distance travelled divided by the time taken. (It is not the average of two speeds !)

AVERAGE VELOCITY Total displacement divided by the time taken. If a particle has position vectors $\mathbf{r}_1$ and $\mathbf{r}_2$ at the beginning and end of the time period t being considered, then the

$$\text{average velocity} = \frac{\mathbf{r}_2 - \mathbf{r}_1}{t}.$$

C

CENTRAL FORCE A force that is directed towards a fixed point and whose magnitude is dependent only on its distance away from the fixed point. For example, the gravitational force on the Earth due to the Sun.

See ***Newton's Law of Gravitation***.

CENTRE OF GRAVITY Suppose a body is composed of n particles whose weights are $\mathbf{w}_1$, $\mathbf{w}_2$, $\mathbf{w}_3$, …, $\mathbf{w}_n$. Then the resultant weight of the body is the vector sum of the weights, i.e. $\sum_{i=1}^{n} \mathbf{w}_i$ and this acts at a point G, say. This point is known as the centre of gravity of the body.

If the body is continuous with its mass distributed throughout its volume, the centre of gravity, G, is still the point at which the resultant weight acts.

The position of the centre of gravity may be found by considering the symmetry of the shape of the body where appropriate, or by using the principle of moments.

Note that G is not necessarily a point belonging to the body; for instance, for a uniform semi-circular arc ABC of radius r, G lies on the axis of symmetry OB distance $2r/\pi$ from O.

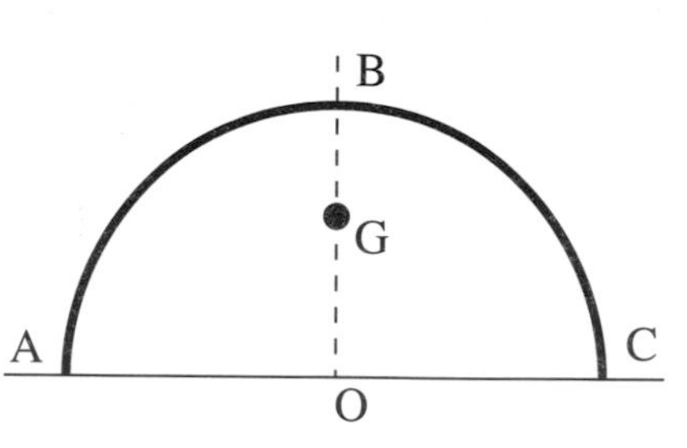

In general, for a body suspended from a point P, the centre of gravity will lie on the vertical line through P; e.g. if the arc ABC above is suspended from the point A and hangs freely, the line AG will be vertical.

The centre of gravity is the same as the centre of mass if the gravitational acceleration is the same on all parts of the body; i.e., for most purposes, when the body is small compared to the size of the Earth, the centre of gravity and the centre of mass coincide.

If the mass of a body is uniformly distributed, then the centre of mass is at the centroid. Thus, for a small body whose mass is uniformly distributed, the centroid, the centre of gravity and the centre of mass are the same point.

CENTRE OF MASS For a system of n particles of mass $m_1, m_2, m_3, \ldots, m_n$ situated at points whose position vectors relative to some origin O are $\mathbf{r}_1, \mathbf{r}_2, \mathbf{r}_3, \ldots, \mathbf{r}_n$, the centre of mass is the mean position vector (i.e. the 'average' position vector) given by

$$\bar{\mathbf{r}} = \frac{\sum_{i=1}^{n} m_i \mathbf{r}_i}{\sum_{i=1}^{n} m_i}.$$

For a body whose mass is uniformly distributed, the centre of mass is at the centroid.

See also ***Centre of Gravity***.

CENTRIFUGAL FORCE An inertial force arising from a centripetal force.

Consider a particle P moving in a horizontal circle as in the case of a conical pendulum.

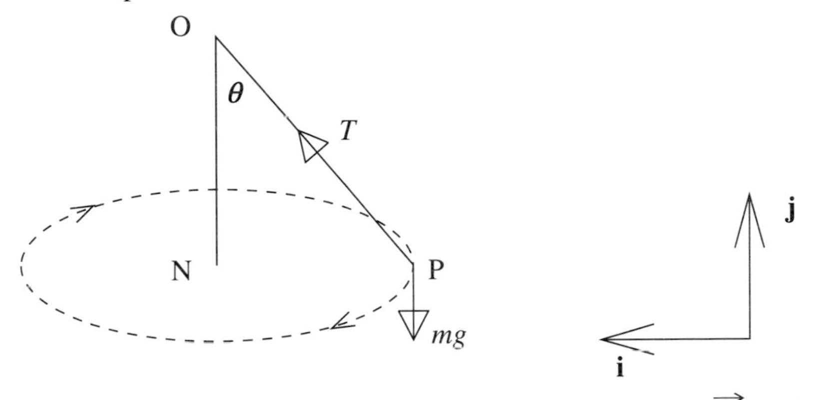

The forces acting on P are the tension T in the direction $\overrightarrow{PO}$ and the weight mg vertically downwards; there is *no other force.*

At least, no other force from the point of view of a stationary observer A. Newton's Second Law gives

$$\begin{pmatrix} T\sin\theta \\ T\cos\theta - mg \end{pmatrix} = m\begin{pmatrix} r\omega^2 \\ 0 \end{pmatrix}.$$

Now consider this situation from the point of view of an observer B moving with P (this is known as an accelerating (non-inertial) frame of reference). Relative to P, (i.e. with P taken as stationary), the acceleration of P (or B) is zero, so the above equations should now be written as

$$\begin{pmatrix} T\sin\theta - mr\omega^2 \\ T\cos\theta - mg \end{pmatrix} = m\begin{pmatrix} 0 \\ 0 \end{pmatrix}$$

and the forces on P may be interpreted as shown in the diagram:–

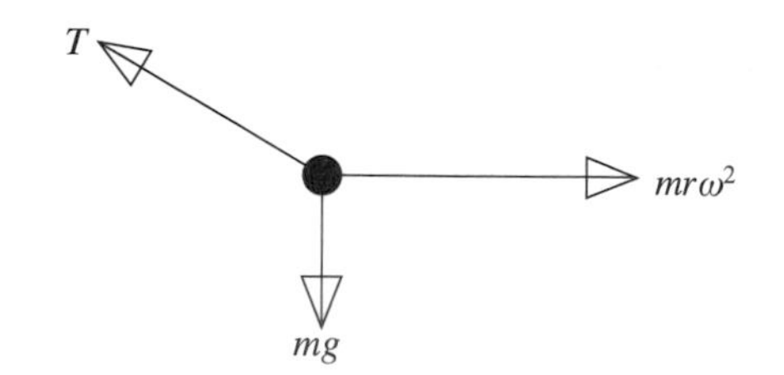

[Note that it is crucial to the argument that the above two sets of equations are both read as 'total force = mass × acceleration' rather than as any rearrangement of this.]

The force '$mr\omega^2$' is called the centrifugal force but in fact only exists for observer B. It does not exist as a force from the viewpoint of A. In fact if the string is cut, the force would not exist for either observer and P would initially travel along the tangent to the circle.

Since all elementary work is done with reference to fixed axes (known as an inertial frame of reference), no inertial forces should be included as forces – they do not exist! The tension and the weight are real forces as a result of the string and the Earth respectively; the term $mr\omega^2$ is a 'mass × acceleration' term. A real (in the sense used above) force is always the result of another object which is easy to identify.

All inertial forces are similar to the above example in that they arise from an equal and opposite real force but are not in themselves real in an inertial frame of reference.

For three very different articles on this subject, see

M. D. Savage (1988) in vol.17 no.3 of Mathematics in School

J. Williams (1988) in vol.17 no.5 of the same journal.

and K. Lord and J. Jagger (1995) *The Mathematical Gazette* **79** (486).

CENTRIPETAL FORCE If a particle P is describing a circle centre O, then the component of the resultant force acting on P in the direction $\overrightarrow{PO}$ is called the centripetal force. It is the force necessary to give the particle the acceleration $\frac{v^2}{r}$ where r is the distance from O to P in the direction $\overrightarrow{PO}$ that is required to maintain its circular motion.

More generally, for a particle P moving along any curved path, the centripetal force is the component of the resultant force acting on P in a direction towards the centre of curvature of the path.

CENTROID The geometric centre of the area (or volume) of a shape. For example, the centroid of a triangle is the point where the medians meet, i.e. the point that divides each median in the ratio 2:1.

See also ***Centre of Gravity, Centre of Mass.***

COEFFICIENT of RESTITUTION (symbol e)

See ***Restitution, Coefficient of***

COMPONENTS OF A FORCE If a force **R** is equivalent to the vector sum of the two forces **P** and **Q**, then these forces are known as components of **R**. We may express this by the vector equation $\mathbf{R} = \mathbf{P} + \mathbf{Q}$, or pictorially thus:–

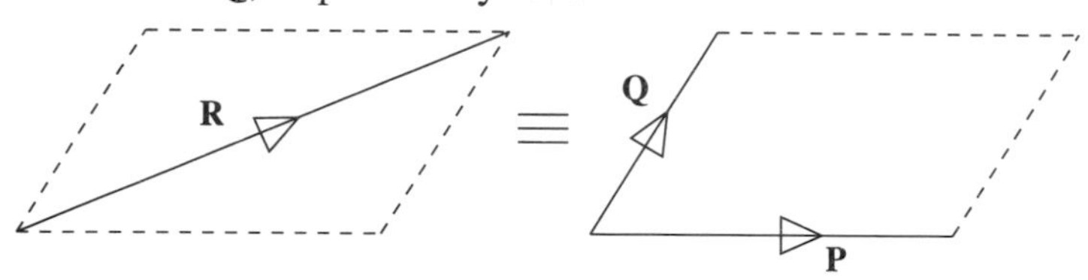

It is usually convenient to resolve **R** into two perpendicular components in specified directions. Suppose the two directions are the x and y axes. Then we have this:–

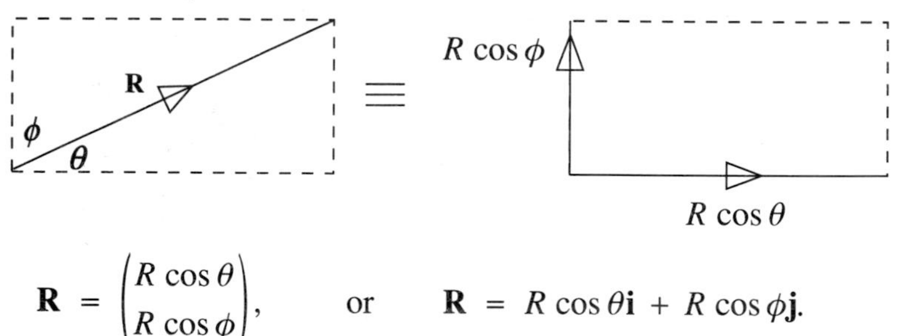

$$\mathbf{R} = \begin{pmatrix} R\cos\theta \\ R\cos\phi \end{pmatrix}, \qquad \text{or} \qquad \mathbf{R} = R\cos\theta\mathbf{i} + R\cos\phi\mathbf{j}.$$

$R\cos\theta$ and $R\cos\phi$ are the components of **R** in the x and y directions respectively. Thus the component of any force in a given direction can be found by using the 'formula'

$$R\cos(\text{angle between } \mathbf{R} \text{ and the given direction})$$

or (and this is the same thing) by using the scalar product $\mathbf{R}.\hat{\mathbf{a}}$ where $\hat{\mathbf{a}}$ is the unit vector in the given direction.

COMPONENTS OF A VECTOR If a vector **a** is equivalent to the two vectors **p** and **q**, so that **a** = **p** + **q**, then **p** and **q** are known as the components of **a**. Usually the components chosen are those in the directions of the x and y axes and so are perpendicular to one another; thus **a** may be expressed as a column vector or in terms of the unit vectors **i** and **j**, for example

$$\mathbf{a} = \begin{pmatrix} p \\ q \end{pmatrix} \qquad \text{or} \qquad \mathbf{a} = p\mathbf{i} + q\mathbf{j}.$$

In this case, the scalars p and q are referred to as the components, their directions being indicated by their positions in the matrix, or by **i** and **j**.

COMPOUND PENDULUM A rigid body fixed at one point and free to rotate about that point in a vertical plane.

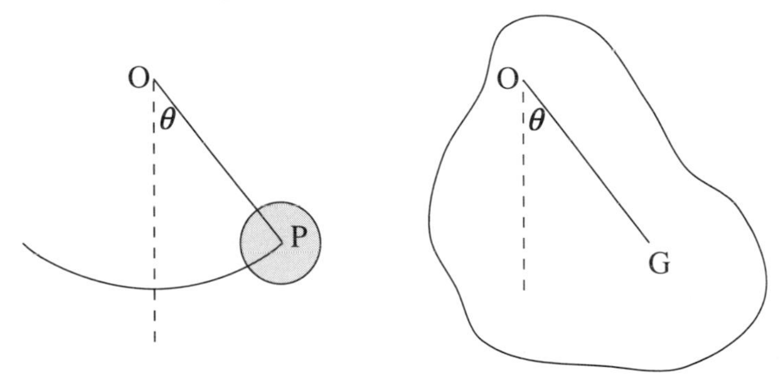

The rigid body may be a heavy rod with a disc at one end like OP or it may be any shape as shown in the second diagram. It oscillates freely below O usually with θ small. (The centre of gravity G of the rigid body must be distinct from the point of suspension O.)

CONICAL PENDULUM A mass suspended by a string from a fixed point O that is travelling in a horizontal circle.

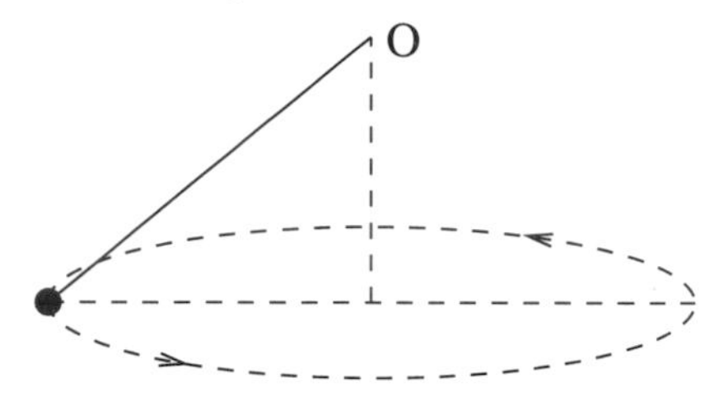

CONSERVATION OF (LINEAR) MOMENTUM When two bodies interact, the total momentum remains constant provided there are no external forces. The two bodies may interact in various ways; situations in which momentum is conserved include collisions, explosions and interactions due to a force of attraction.

CONSERVATIVE FORCE A force that does no net work on a body when it moves from one position A to another position B and then back again to A. This is true irrespective of the paths chosen from A to B and from B to A.

For example, the force of gravity is a conservative force – consider a ball moving vertically upwards from A to B and then back down again to A. Suppose the distance AB $= h$.

For the displacement AB, the work done by gravity $= -mgh$ (negative because the force is in the opposite direction to the motion).

For the displacement BA, the work done by gravity $= mgh$.
Thus, the total work done $= -mgh + mgh = 0$.

Another example, this time of a force that is not conservative, is friction. Imagine an object sliding along a rough table from A to B and back again to A.

Work done by friction F from A to B = $-\,\mathrm{F}h$ (where h = AB).

Work done by F from B to A = $-\,\mathrm{F}h$ (again the force opposes the motion).

So total work done = $(-\,\mathrm{F}h) + (-\,\mathrm{F}h) = -2\mathrm{F}h$.

Thus friction is not conservative.

Note that when friction is acting, some of the energy of the ball is lost in the form of heat and sound. Whereas with a conservative force the work done by the force has the effect of converting potential energy (PE) into kinetic energy (KE) or vice versa.

CONSTANT ACCELERATION EQUATIONS These are usually given in their one-dimensional form:–

$$v = u + at \qquad s = \tfrac{1}{2}(u + v)t$$

$$s = ut + \tfrac{1}{2}at^2 \qquad v^2 = u^2 + 2as$$

where a is the constant acceleration and s the displacement from the origin. Before you use these, check that in the situation given, the acceleration really is constant.

But they are valid as vector equations in two and three dimensions provided the vector acceleration **a** is constant (i.e. in magnitude *and* direction). The corresponding vector equations are :–

$$\mathbf{v} = \mathbf{u} + t\mathbf{a} \qquad \mathbf{r} = \tfrac{1}{2}(\mathbf{u} + \mathbf{v})t$$

$$\mathbf{r} = t\mathbf{u} + \tfrac{1}{2}t^2\mathbf{a} \qquad v^2 = u^2 + 2\mathbf{a.r}$$

$$(\text{or } \mathbf{v.v} = \mathbf{u.u} + 2\mathbf{a.r})$$

where the ‘dot’ indicates that the scalar product of the vectors should be found.

COUPLE Two equal and opposite parallel forces not acting through the same point.

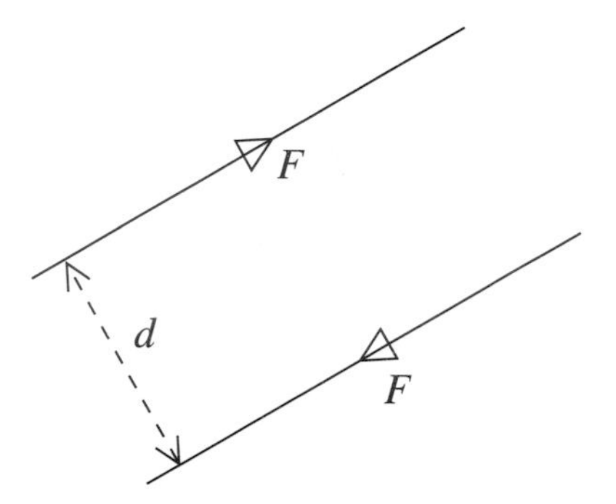

If the forces have magnitude F and their lines of action are distance d apart, then the moment of the couple about any point in the plane of the two forces has magnitude Fd; the direction (in the case above) being clockwise.

Two coplanar couples are equivalent, i.e. have the same rotational effect, if their moments have the same magnitude and direction (both clockwise or both anticlockwise).

In three dimensions, the moment of a couple is a vector quantity, the magnitude being defined as above and the direction being perpendicular to the plane of the forces. In the diagram above, the direction of the vector is perpendicular to the page and into the page, according to the right-hand screw rule.

See ***vector product.***

D

DENSITY The mass per unit volume of a material. For an object of volume V of mass m made of a uniform material, density $\rho = \frac{m}{V}$. Units are kg m^{-3}.

DISPLACEMENT-TIME GRAPH A graph that illustrates the displacement of an object which is travelling in a straight line at various times. The x-axis is used for the time measurements.

The gradient of the graph gives the velocity of the object.

These graphs are sometimes called distance-time graphs; strictly speaking, this is incorrect because the distance on the y-axis, being positive or negative, must be a one-dimensional vector and hence a displacement.

Note that it is not possible, on two-dimensional paper, to have a displacement-time graph where the displacements are more than one-dimensional, so these graphs can only be drawn for objects travelling in straight lines.

DISTANCE-TIME GRAPH See *Displacement-time Graph*.

DYNAMIC EQUILIBRIUM See *Equilibrium*.

E

ELASTIC IMPACT An impact for which the coefficient of restitution is 1.

See also ***Newton's Experimental Law***.

ELASTICITY, MODULUS OF (symbol λ) A measure of how easy it is to stretch an elastic string (or spring). If the tension is measured by Hooke's Law with $T = \frac{\lambda x}{l}$, then λ is the magnitude of the tension when the string is twice its natural length.

See also ***Hooke's Law***.

ELASTIC POTENTIAL ENERGY (EPE) The energy stored in a string or spring when it is stretched. A spring also has EPE when it is compressed.

If the tension in an elastic string (spring) of natural length l and modulus of elasticity λ is $\frac{\lambda x}{l}$, then the EPE is $\frac{\lambda x^2}{2l}$, where x is the extension.

See also ***Potential Energy***.

ENERGY Energy is a quantity which manifests itself in a variety of forms – heat, light and sound are examples – but in mechanics, we are concerned only with mechanical energy, i.e. kinetic energy and potential energy.

Kinetic energy (KE) is the energy a particle has that is due to its speed. It is calculated from the formula $\frac{1}{2}mv^2$, which is sometimes written as the scalar product $\frac{1}{2}m\mathbf{v}.\mathbf{v}$.

For a rigid body, there may be kinetic energy due to its angular speed ω as well as its linear speed. Thus its total kinetic energy is

$$\tfrac{1}{2}mv^2 + \tfrac{1}{2}I\omega^2$$

where I is the moment of inertia about the axis of rotation.

Potential energy (PE) is the energy a body has that is due to its position. It is the result of a conservative force and is the work done by that force in moving the body from its present position to the position of zero potential energy.

The formula for potential energy depends upon the conservative force involved.

Energy is a scalar quantity; the SI unit is the joule (J).

See also ***Potential Energy, Energy Conservation, Work-energy Equation***.

ENERGY CONSERVATION, ENERGY PRINCIPLE If the forces which act on a system are conservative or if they are such that they do no work during the motion, then the total mechanical energy is constant.

i.e. kinetic energy + potential energy = constant.

If A and B are any two convenient positions of the body during the motion, then a useful form of the energy principle is

$$\text{Total (KE + PE) at A} = \text{total (KE + PE) at B}$$

Note that in the above principle, the term 'energy' means mechanical energy, i.e. kinetic energy and potential energy. If all types of energy arc included, e.g. light, heat, etc. then there is a very important and more global energy principle which states that the total energy in any system is constant.

EQUATION OF MOTION An equation (usually a differential equation) that states the law governing how a body moves. The phrase 'equation of motion' in mechanics usually means Newton's Second Law

$$\mathbf{F} = m\mathbf{a} = m\frac{d\mathbf{v}}{dt}.$$

EQUILIBRIUM A particle is in equilibrium if the vector sum of the forces acting on it is zero. This is equivalent to the (linear) acceleration being zero. Thus, a body is in equilibrium if

(1) it is at rest and remains at rest – this is static equilibrium,

(2) it moves with constant velocity – this is dynamic equilibrium.

A rigid body (an extended body that cannot be modelled as a particle) is in equilibrium if both (a) the vector sum of the forces acting on it is zero and (b) the total moment of all the forces about any point or axis is zero. This is equivalent to the linear and angular accelerations both being zero.

F

FICTITIOUS FORCE The same as an inertial force – see ***Centrifugal Force***.

FORCE That which pushes or pulls, attracts or repels. Newton's Second Law of motion defines force as the rate of change of momentum. Force is a vector quantity and therefore can be added, subtracted and multiplied by a scalar in exactly the same way as vectors.

The SI unit of force is the newton (N).

The sum of any number of forces is interpreted as the combined effect of the forces and is called the resultant. The triangle of forces and the parallelogram of forces are ways of adding two forces. The polygon of forces is an extension of the triangle of forces for adding more than two forces; but for more than two forces, it is easier to resolve them into components in two perpendicular directions and then add them.

If $\mathbf{X}$ and $\mathbf{Y}$ are the sums of the components in the two directions, the resultant of $\mathbf{X}$ and $\mathbf{Y}$ will be the resultant $\mathbf{R}$ of the original set of forces. Thus $\mathbf{R} = \mathbf{X} + \mathbf{Y}$.

FORCE OF GRAVITY See ***Newton's Law of Gravitation***.

See also ***Mass and Weight***.

FRAME OF REFERENCE See ***Inertial Frame of Reference***.

FRAMEWORK See ***Light Framework***.

FREE VECTOR A vector whose position is not specified. It is represented by a line segment which may be placed anywhere. Most vectors are free; a position vector is an example of one that is not.

FREELY HINGED, SMOOTHLY HINGED This implies that the action of the hinge on the body is a single force (rather than a force and a couple).

FRICTION The force that resists the motion of one surface sliding over another.

Consider a stationary particle on a rough horizontal plane being pulled horizontally by a gradually increasing force P.

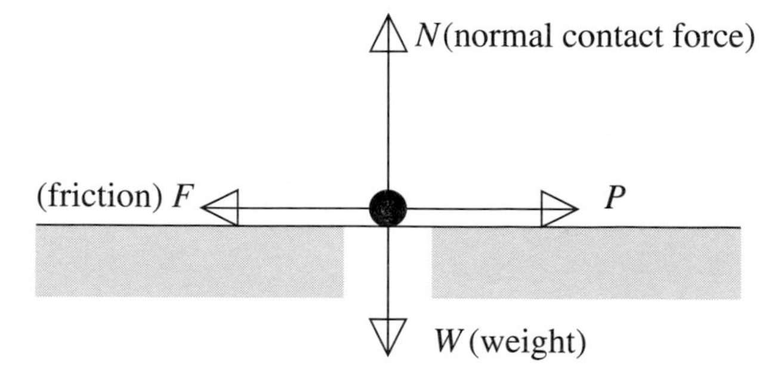

Where P is small, the friction set up to oppose the intended movement will be just sufficient to maintain equilibrium, i.e. $P = F$. As P is increased, F also increases to maintain equilibrium until F reaches its maximum value F_{max}. If P is made still larger, F can no longer increase to oppose the motion and P succeeds in pulling the particle across the plane, i.e. equilibrium is broken since now $P > F_{max}$.

The magnitude of F_{max} is usually taken to be μN where μ is the coefficient of (static) friction.

When $P = F_{max} = \mu N$, and with the particle still at rest though on the point of moving, it is said to be in *limiting equilibrium.*

If the particle is actually sliding over the surface, it is often assumed that the force of friction remains at its maximum value of μN – in fact, it decreases slightly since the coefficient of kinetic friction μ' is slightly less than μ.

The value of μ depends upon the nature of the two surfaces in contact. Typical values are:–

Metal on metal	0.15 to 0.3
Wood on wood	0.2 to 0.5
Masonry on masonry	0.5 to 0.7

N.B. The condition $F_{max} = \mu N$ is an experimental law and appears to be valid where N is (relatively) small and in a limited number of situations.

Let us now consider surfaces in more detail – under a microscope, as it were. Consider a block lying on a table and suppose there is no tendency for it to slide. The surface in contact will not be smooth and we can model the situation with a lot of normal contact forces as shown:–

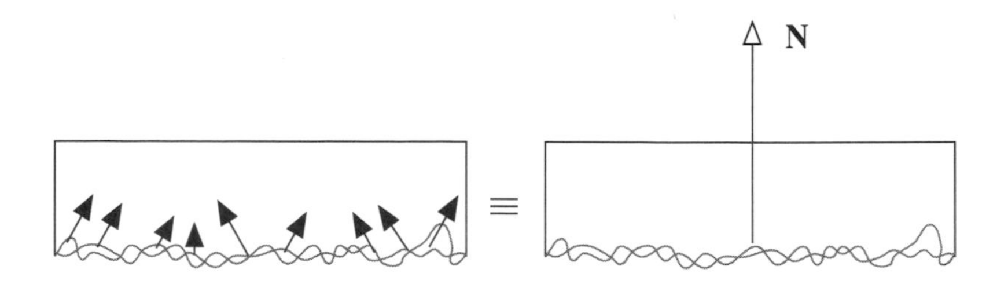

The overall effect (i.e. the sum of these) will be a force **N** at right angles to the table. But if the block is being pushed to the left, then these contact forces will add up to a resultant force which will not be at right angles to the table – see next diagram:–

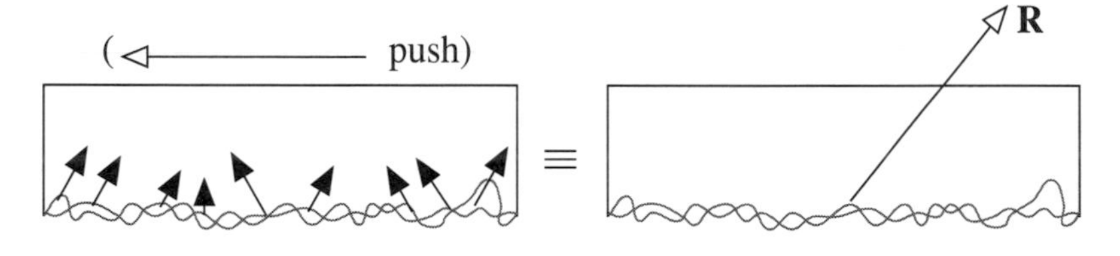

This force **R** we call the total contact force. It is this force that we usually think of in its two components – the normal contact force and the friction – see the diagram below:–

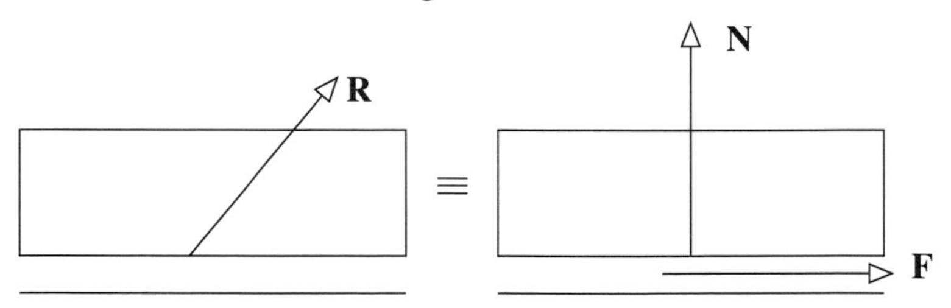

Thus our notion of friction is merely a convenient way of thinking about that component of **R** that we associate with the force that resists sliding.

G

g The acceleration due to the force of gravity and equal to 9.81 m s^{-2} (to 3 significant figures) on the Earth's surface.

On the surface of the Moon, its value is 1.62 m s^{-2} (to 3 s.f.).

See ***Mass and Weight***.

GRAVITATIONAL AND INERTIAL MASS The mass of a body is often defined as the quantity of matter in the body. This can be viewed in two distinct ways depending upon how it is measured:

1) If we measure it by weighing it, we are finding its 'gravitational mass' i.e. a quantity proportional to the gravitational force between the Earth and the body.
2) If we measure it by finding the force required to give it an acceleration of 1 m s^{-2} we are finding its 'inertial mass'. This is done by using Newton's Second Law $F = ma$ with $a = 1$ to give $m \times 1 = F$. This is the property of the body which is associated with its reluctance to being accelerated. The word 'inertia' is often used to express this property.

In Newtonian mechanics, the values of the gravitational and inertial masses of a body are indistinguishable and so we refer to the 'mass' of a body without the need to specify which.

GRAVITATIONAL CONSTANT (G) The universal constant appearing in Newton's Law of Gravitation.

$$G = 6.672 \times 10^{-11}\ \mathrm{Nm}^2\ \mathrm{kg}^{-2}.$$

This is also called the 'universal gravitational constant'.

GRAVITATIONAL POTENTIAL ENERGY (GPE) The energy that a body has that is due to its position. It is the result of the force of gravity.

If the force of gravity is assumed to be constant and equal to mg, then its gravitational potential energy is mgh where h is the vertical height of the centre of gravity of the body above the level of zero PE.

If the force of gravity is given by Newton's Law of Gravitation, then $|\mathbf{F}| = \dfrac{GMm}{r^2}$ and the potential energy $= \dfrac{GMm}{r}$ where r is the distance of the body, mass m, from the centre of the Earth, mass M, (or any other massive object).

The first model for gravity is appropriate for distances close to the surface of the Earth. This is valid even at the top of Everest, 8.848 km above sea-level. The second model for gravity is necessary for objects in space, e.g. satellites.

See ***Potential Energy.***

GRAVITY The word refers to both the acceleration of a mass due to the force of gravity and also to the force of gravity itself. This sometimes leads to confusion. The acceleration due to gravity is the same for all masses and is denoted by 'g' where $g = 9.8\ \mathrm{m\ s}^{-2}$ (2 s.f.) at the surface of the Earth; the force of gravity depends on the mass, and is $m \times 9.8$ (i.e. mg) newtons.

H

HOOKE'S LAW An experimental law which states that the magnitude of the tension T in a stretched string, or spring, is proportional to the extension x, i.e. $T \alpha x$.

The law is used in the form $T = kx$ where k is the 'stiffness' of the string/spring, or in the form $T = \frac{\lambda x}{l}$ where l is its natural length and λ its modulus of elasticity. Note therefore that $k = \frac{\lambda}{l}$.

Hooke's Law is not usually valid if x is relatively large, since the string may lose its elasticity and will not return to its natural length.

Hooke's Law is named after the English physicist Robert Hooke (1638-1703).

I

IMPULSE The impulse of a force **F** acting for a time t is the quantity $t\mathbf{F}$ (or $\int \mathbf{F}dt$ if **F** is not constant).

Impulse is a vector quantity; the SI unit is the kg m s^{-1}.

This quantity arises when Newton's Second Law of motion is integrated with respect to time:

$$\mathbf{F} = m\frac{dv}{dt}$$

$$\therefore \int_0^t \mathbf{F}\,dt = \int_u^v m\,d\mathbf{v} = m\mathbf{v} - m\mathbf{u}$$

or if the force **F** is constant,

$$t\mathbf{F} = m\mathbf{v} - m\mathbf{u}$$

i.e. impulse of a force = final momentum – initial momentum

or impulse = change in momentum.

The impulse of a force is therefore often found indirectly by finding the change in the momentum. This is particularly useful when the force and time are unknown, but the momentum before and afterwards can be measured, for example in a collision.

IMPULSE-MOMENTUM EQUATION This is the name given to the equation

impulse = change in momentum

See also ***Impulse***.

INELASTIC IMPACT An impact for which the coefficient of restitution is zero.

See also ***Elastic Impact***.

INERTIA More properly inertial mass.

See ***Gravitational and Inertial Mass, Moment of Inertia***.

INERTIAL FORCE See ***Centrifugal Force***, which is an example of an inertial force.

INERTIAL FRAME OF REFERENCE A coordinate system in which Newton's First Law is valid. Any other frame which moves with constant velocity relative to this frame will also be inertial. The standard inertial frame is a set of axes fixed in space relative to the position of distant stars. A set of axes fixed on the Earth's surface is considered to be a good approximation to an inertial frame.

INERTIAL MASS See ***Gravitational and Inertial Mass***.

J

JOULE (J) The SI unit of work and energy equal to one newton metre. It is named after the English physicist J. P. Joule (1818 – 1889).

K

KILOGRAM (kg) The SI unit of mass. It is defined as the mass of a certain cylinder of platinum and iridium kept at Sèvres in France.

KINEMATICS The study of the motion of particles or bodies without reference to mass or force. Kinematics is thus concerned only with position, velocity and acceleration.

KINETIC ENERGY (KE) The energy a particle has that is due to its speed – either its linear speed or its angular speed or both. KE is a scalar quantity and does not depend upon the direction of motion.

The KE of a particle is $\frac{1}{2}mv^2$, sometimes written as the scalar product $\frac{1}{2}m\mathbf{v}.\mathbf{v}$.

The KE of a rigid body rotating about a fixed axis with angular speed ω is $\frac{1}{2}I\omega^2$ where I is the moment of inertia about the axis of rotation.

The SI unit of kinetic energy is the joule (J).

KNOT A speed of one nautical mile per hour.

See also ***Nautical Mile***.

L

LAMINA A thin (usually plane) sheet of rigid material whose thickness is negligible.

LAMI'S THEOREM If three forces acting at a point are in equilibrium then

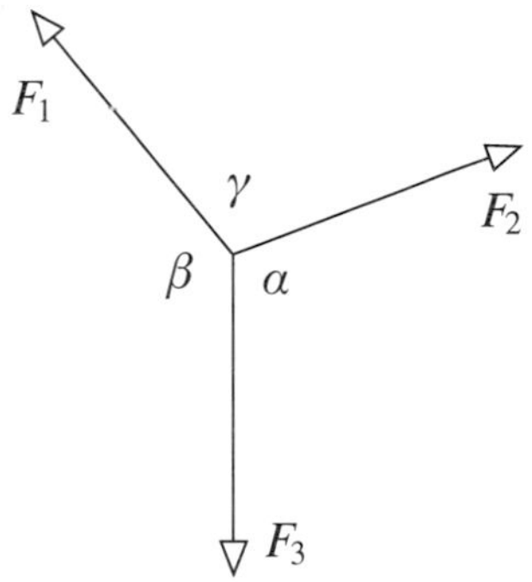

$$\frac{F_1}{\sin \alpha} = \frac{F_2}{\sin \beta} = \frac{F_3}{\sin \gamma}$$

This is a consequence of the Sine Rule used in the corresponding triangle of forces:–

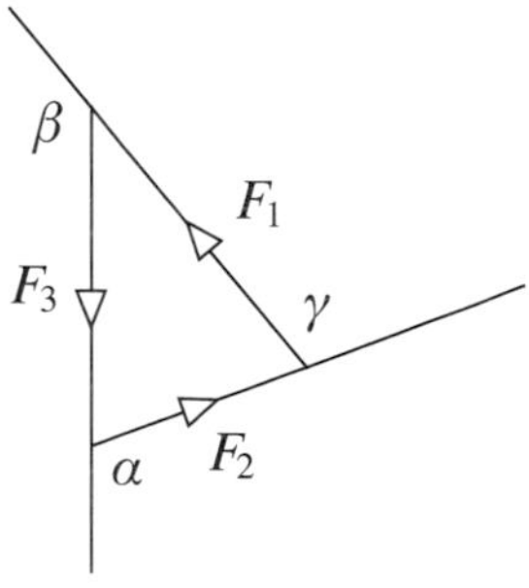

This theorem was published by B. Lami in 1679.

LIGHT Having negligible weight (in comparison to other parts of the system under consideration), e.g. a light rod is one whose weight can be ignored.

LIGHT FRAMEWORK A framework of light rods that are jointed together to form a rigid construction.

See also ***Strut, Tie***.

LIMITING EQUILIBRIUM See ***Friction***.

LINEAR MOMENTUM Momentum that is due to linear (rather than angular) velocity.

LINEAR VELOCITY Velocity along a line, curved or straight – in contrast to angular velocity.

LOCALIZED (OR TIED) VECTOR A vector whose position is specified, e.g. a position vector, a force.

See ***Free Vector***.

M

MASS AND WEIGHT The mass of a body is its quantity of matter. It is related to its volume and density by the equation

$$\text{mass} = \text{volume} \times \text{density}.$$

It is a scalar quantity and the SI unit is the kilogram (kg).

For more detailed information about mass, see ***Gravitational and Inertial Mass***.

The weight of a body is the force on the body due to the gravitational pull of the Earth. By Newton's Law of Gravitation the magnitude of the force on a mass m at the Earth's surface is given by

$$F = \frac{\mathrm{G}Mm}{R^2}$$

where $M = 5{\cdot}98 \times 10^{24}$ kg is the mass of the Earth, R is the radius of the Earth at the point on the Earth's surface and G is the gravitational constant equal to $6{\cdot}672 \times 10^{-11}\ \mathrm{N\,m^2\,kg^2}$.

Comparing $F = \dfrac{\mathrm{G}Mm}{R^2} = m\left(\dfrac{\mathrm{G}M}{R^2}\right)$, with Newton's Second Law, $F = ma$, we obtain the magnitude of the acceleration due to gravity, $g = \dfrac{\mathrm{G}M}{R^2}$ (at the surface of the Earth).

The value of g therefore varies over the surface of the Earth depending on the value of R:–

In London $g = 9{\cdot}81 \text{ ms}^{-2}$

At the North Pole $g = 9{\cdot}83 \text{ ms}^{-2}$

At the Equator $g = 9{\cdot}78 \text{ ms}^{-2}$

At the top of Everest (8 848 m above sea level)

$$g = 9{\cdot}77 \text{ ms}^{-2}$$

Thus weight = mg where $g = 9{\cdot}8 \text{ ms}^{-2}$ (2 s.f.).

There is a confusion of language with mass and weight because mass is found by 'weighing' the object. The 'weight' (as it is normally called) obtained is actually the mass because of the way in which the scales are calibrated. For instance, a single apple weighs about 0·25 lb. or 100 grams. In ordinary language, this is its 'weight'. In fact this is its mass and its weight is 0.1g N or approximately 1 newton.

MECHANICAL ENERGY Kinetic energy and potential energy.

See also ***Energy***.

METRE (m) The SI unit of length that, since 1983, is defined as the length of the path travelled by light in a vacuum during the time

$$\frac{1}{299\,792\,458} \text{ seconds}.$$

See also ***Speed of light***.

METRIC TON The unit of mass equal to 1000 kilograms. It is now known as the 'tonne'.

MODEL, MODELLING This word has a variety of slightly different meanings:–

1) Newton's Second law is the accepted model for how force, acceleration and mass are related. It is universally valid. (The fact that this model is a simplification of the more sophisticated model of Einstein's does not detract from its universality.)

2) The friction law $F = \mu N$ is a model for the maximum value of the force of friction between some surfaces and is valid for a limited range of N. This 'law' is experimental, not exact and lacks the universality of Newton's Laws of Motion; for instance in geology, where N is often very large, the law is closer to

$$F_{\max} = \mu\sqrt{N}.$$

3) When we use mechanics to solve real problems, then necessarily simplifications and assumptions have to be made. e.g. a string may be supposed to be light and inextensible, it may be assumed that the tension in an elastic string obeys Hooke's Law – an experimental law which is not always true.

   This is all part of 'setting up a model' or 'modelling the situation'; other modelling activities include drawing a diagram and indicating the forces (this may also involve making some simplifications or assumptions).

The reason for this modelling process is to make the problem amenable to mathematical analysis. It is also necessary to make the problem easy enough to solve given the mathematical background of the problem-solver, e.g. initially students may assume that a ball (for instance) thrown in the air travels under the action of gravity alone, whereas later, the model may be refined to include the effects of air resistance.

The art of good modelling is to make the original problem easy enough to solve while still producing a solution that reflects the main features of the original problem.

MOMENT OF A FORCE The turning or rotational effect of a force. In two dimensions, if the force **F** acts at point A in the direction shown in the diagram below, the moment of **F** about an axis through the point O at right angles to the plane of the paper

$$= |\mathbf{F}| \times \mathrm{ON} \text{ in an anticlockwise sense.}$$

(Note that this is usually said to be 'the moment of the force **F** about the point O' – but the precise formulation is that above.)

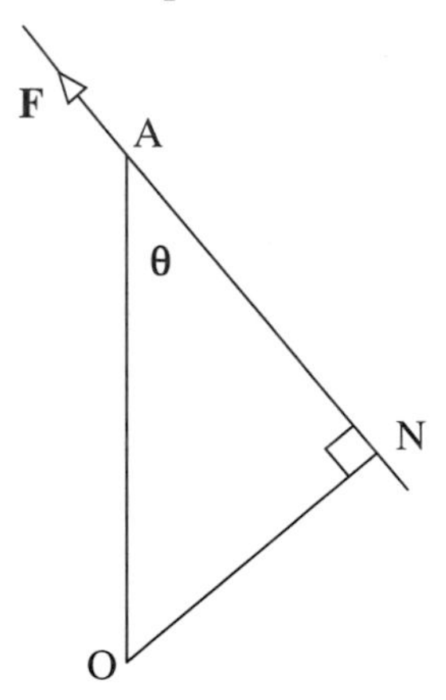

A and N are on the line of action of the force **F** so ON is the perpendicular distance of the line of action of the force **F** from the point O.

The moment of a force may be clockwise or anticlockwise, so we regard one of these directions as positive and the other negative.

To take moments about an axis through a point (or loosely, to take moments about a point) means that we find the sum of the moments of the various forces about that point, with due regard to direction. If the system is in equilibrium, the sum of the moments is zero.

In three dimensions, the plane in which the turning effect of the force occurs must be stated, or equivalently, the direction of the axis of rotation. This is neatly achieved by defining the moment of a force **F** about a point O as the vector product

$$\mathbf{r} \times \mathbf{F} \qquad \text{(where } \mathbf{r} = \overrightarrow{OA} \text{ in the diagram above).}$$

Note that (1) $\mathbf{r} \times \mathbf{F}$ is perpendicular to both $\mathbf{r}$ and $\mathbf{F}$, and therefore parallel to the axis of rotation.

and (2) $|\mathbf{r} \times \mathbf{F}| = |\mathbf{F}| \times \text{OA} \sin\theta = |\mathbf{F}| \times \text{ON}$ as before.

The resultant moment about O of all the forces acting on a body is the vector sum of all the terms $\mathbf{r} \times \mathbf{F}$.

Just as the resultant force is the rate of change of (linear) momentum, so the resultant moment is the rate of change of angular momentum of the body.

In more advanced work, there may be a variety of forces acting on a rigid body, but the body may be constrained so that it can rotate only about a fixed axis. In this case, only the component of the moment $\mathbf{r} \times \mathbf{F}$ about O which is parallel to the fixed axis will contribute to the turning effect about that axis.

If $\hat{\mathbf{a}}$ is the unit vector parallel to the axis, then the component of $\mathbf{r} \times \mathbf{F}$ required is $(\mathbf{r} \times \mathbf{F}).\hat{\mathbf{a}}$. Thus, in three dimensions we distinguish between (a) the moment of $\mathbf{F}$ about a point $= \mathbf{r} \times \mathbf{F}$, and (b) the moment of $\mathbf{F}$ about an axis $= (\mathbf{r} \times \mathbf{F}).\hat{\mathbf{a}}$.

MOMENT OF INERTIA (symbol I) A quantity which depends upon the distribution of the mass in a rigid body. If the body consists of n particles of mass m_i where $1 \leqslant i \leqslant n$ and if the perpendicular distance of these particles from an axis is r_i respectively, then the moment of inertia of the body about the axis is given by

$$I = \sum_{i=1}^{n} m_i r_i^2 .$$

Thus a body with most of its mass concentrated near its centre will have a smaller value of I than a body with the same total mass but whose distribution is much further from the centre.

The moment of inertia is sometimes written in the form

$$I = Mk^2$$

where the total mass of the body $M = \sum m_i$, and k is known as the radius of gyration, whose magnitude is defined by $Mk^2 = \sum_{i=1}^{n} m_i r_i^2$.

The moment of inertia for a rotating rigid body is the property of the body which is associated with its reluctance to having its angular velocity changed – this compares with the role of mass which is the property of a body associated with its reluctance to having its linear velocity changed.

See also ***Angular Momentum, Gravitational and Inertial Mass***.

MOMENT OF MOMENTUM This is the same as angular momentum.

MOMENTUM The 'quantity of motion' measured by multiplying the mass of a body by its velocity, i.e. $m\mathbf{v}$. Momentum is a vector quantity which depends upon both the speed and the direction of motion.

The SI unit for momentum is the kg m s^{-1}.

It is sometimes referred to as linear momentum to distinguish it from angular momentum.

N

NAUTICAL MILE 1852 metres or 1.15 miles.

A nautical mile was originally a length equal to the distance on the surface of the Earth corresponding to an angle of 1' (i.e. $\frac{1}{60}$ of a degree) at the centre of the Earth. This distance varies from approximately 2 004 metres at the poles to 1 984 metres at the equator. In the UK, the value of 6 082 feet (1 854 metres) was eventually adopted. In 1929, the international nautical mile was defined as 1 852 metres; officially this has now superseded the other variants.

NEUTRAL EQUILIBRIUM A position of static equilibrium such that if the body is slightly moved, then it will remain in its new position, since this is also an equilibrium position.

See also ***stable equilibrium, unstable equilibrium***.

NEWTON (N) The SI unit of force equal to the magnitude of the force required to give a mass of one kilogram an acceleration of magnitude 1 m s^{-2}. The weight of a small apple is about one newton. It is named after the English mathematician and physicist Sir Isaac Newton (1642 - 1727).

NEWTONIAN MECHANICS Mechanics based on Newton's Laws of Motion. It is also known as 'classical mechanics' to distinguish it from

1) relativistic mechanics which is an appropriate model when discussing the motion of objects moving with speeds which approach the speed of light, or from
2) quantum mechanics which is the model used for understanding the behaviour of atomic and sub-atomic particles.

Newtonian mechanics is essential for many physics and engineering problems in the ordinary terrestrial setting. It analyses forces and motion, and forms part of physics where the physical situation is stressed, and a part of applied mathematics where the physical situation is analysed mathematically.

NEWTON'S EXPERIMENTAL LAW (NEL) Consider two masses m_1, m_2 colliding directly (i.e. travelling in the same straight line) with speeds u_1, u_2 so that after the collision, their speeds are v_1, v_2 respectively.

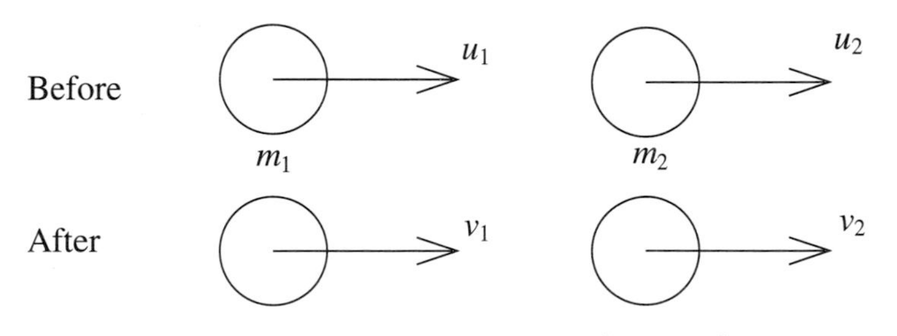

Then NEL states that $v_1 - v_2 = -e(u_1 - u_2)$ where e is a constant known as the coefficient of restitution; $0 \leqslant e \leqslant 1$.

If the speeds involved are not in the same straight line as illustrated above, so that the impact is oblique, the law still holds for the components of the velocities parallel to the line of centres (i.e. the line joining the two centres). The components of the velocities perpendicular to the line of centres are unchanged by the impact if there is no friction.

The value of e is determined by the nature of the materials involved in the collision.

See ***elastic impact***.

NEWTON'S LAW OF GRAVITATION If two bodies of mass m_1 and m_2 are separated by a distance r, they will attract each other by a force of magnitude $F = \dfrac{Gm_1m_2}{r^2}$ where $G = 6{\cdot}672 \times 10^{-11}\ \mathrm{Nm^2\,kg^{-2}}$ is the universal gravitational constant.

This law was published by Newton in 1687; he was the first to realise that the force which keeps the Moon moving around the Earth is the same as that which causes objects to fall to the ground.

NEWTON'S LAWS OF MOTION The three fundamental laws of motion published in 1687.

If the resultant external force on a body is zero, then the body moves with constant velocity (i.e. constant speed in a straight line).

Thus a force is only required to *change* a velocity; in order to maintain a constant velocity, the total force must be zero. Note that the constant velocity may, of course, be zero so that a body at rest must also be experiencing no resultant external force.

The rate of change of momentum of a body is proportional to the resultant, external force and takes place in the direction of this force, i.e.

$$\frac{d\,(m\mathbf{v})}{dt}\ \alpha\ \mathbf{F} \qquad \text{or} \qquad \frac{d\,(m\mathbf{v})}{dt} = k\,\mathbf{F}$$

where k is a constant.

By choosing the unit of force to be the newton, we make $k = 1$ so that $\dfrac{d\,(m\mathbf{v})}{dt} = \mathbf{F}$.

The mass m is usually constant so Newton's Second Law becomes

$$m\,\frac{d\mathbf{v}}{dt} = \mathbf{F} \qquad \text{or} \qquad \mathbf{F} = m\mathbf{a}$$

where **a** is the acceleration.

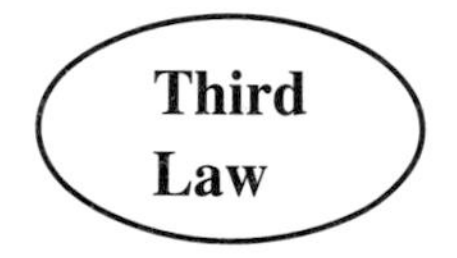

Considering two bodies A and B, the force exerted by body A upon body B is equal and opposite to the force exerted by B on A.

NORMAL CONTACT FORCE, NORMAL REACTION

The component of the total contact force between two surfaces which is at right angles to those surfaces at the point of contact.

In the diagram below, **R** is the total contact force on the block due to the plane, **N** is the normal contact force perpendicular to the plane and **F** the other component of **R**, usually due to friction.

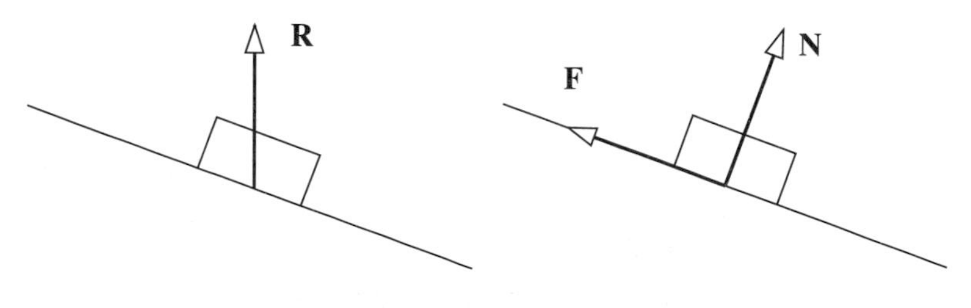

P

PARALLEL-AXIS THEOREM If the moment of inertia of a body of mass M about an axis through the centre of mass is I_G, then the moment of inertia about a parallel axis is given by

$$I = I_G + Mh^2$$

where h is the perpendicular distance between the two axes. This theorem applies to both solid and plane shapes.

See also ***the perpendicular axis theorem.***

PARALLELOGRAM OF FORCES If two forces are represented in magnitude and direction by the sides AB and AD of a parallelogram, then the diagonal AC represents the sum, or resultant, of these forces.

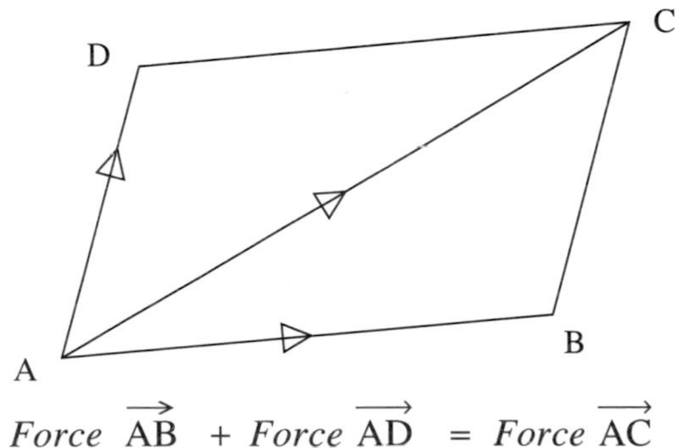

$$Force\ \overrightarrow{AB} + Force\ \overrightarrow{AD} = Force\ \overrightarrow{AC}$$

See also ***triangle of forces, polygon of forces***.

PARTICLE A body with mass but no dimensions, so that it is represented by a mathematical point. The importance of modelling a body as a particle is that, necessarily, all the forces acting on the body are concurrent and act at that point representing the position of the body. As a result, the motion of the body is completely governed by Newton's Second Law $\mathbf{F} = m\mathbf{a}$; there is no rotational motion.

Many bodies may often be assumed to be particles if their linear size is small compared with the linear dimensions of the space in which they move.

See also ***rigid body***.

PASCAL (Pa) The SI unit of pressure equal to 1 newton per square metre. It is named after the French mathematician Blaise Pascal (1623-1662)

PERFECTLY ELASTIC A collision is said to be perfectly elastic if the coefficient of restitution $e = 1$. In this case, no energy is lost by the impact.

See also ***elastic impact***.

PERFECTLY INELASTIC A collision is said to be perfectly inelastic if the coefficient of restitution is zero.

See also ***elastic impact***.

PERIOD, PERIODIC TIME The time taken for a complete oscillation. For example, if a particle is moving with Simple Harmonic Motion governed by the equation $\frac{d^2x}{dt^2} = -\omega^2 x$, where ω is a constant, then the period of the motion is $\frac{2\pi}{\omega}$.

PERPENDICULAR-AXIS THEOREM For a lamina, if the moments of inertia of the lamina about two perpendicular axes in the plane of the lamina are I_X and I_Y respectively, then the moment of inertia, I_Z, of the lamina about an axis at right angles to the plane of the lamina is given by

$$I_Z = I_X + I_Y.$$

N.B. This theorem cannot be applied to solid bodies, only to laminae. Also, the three axes must be mutually perpendicular and concurrent.

See also the ***parallel-axis theorem***.

POLYGON OF FORCES A polygon of forces is used for adding more than two forces. For example, suppose there are four coplanar forces with magnitudes 1.5, 2, 3, 4, newtons acting on a particle in the directions shown:

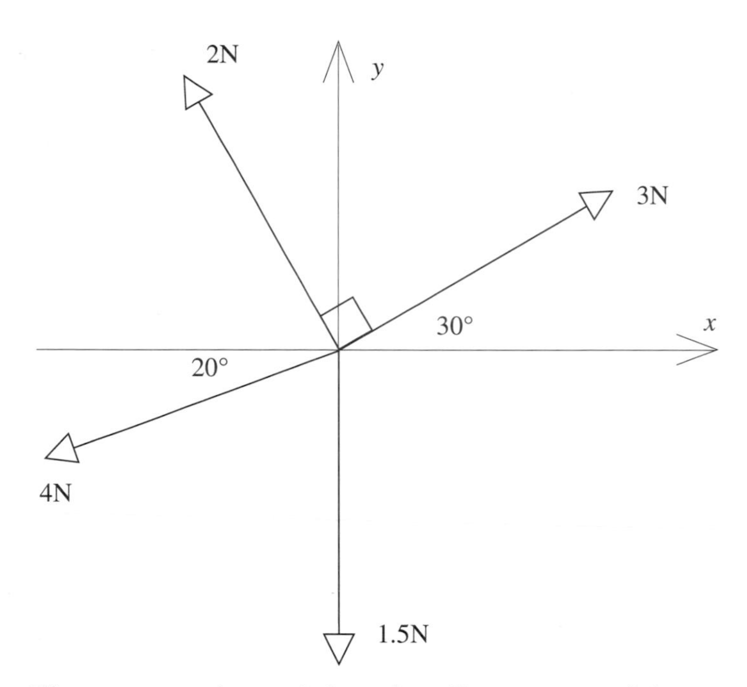

Then, representing each force by a line segment of the appropriate length, they can be added by joining the line segments end on and completing the polygon.

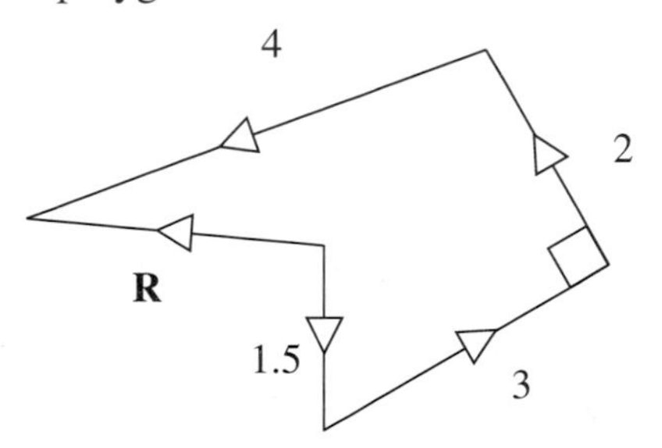

In this case, the polygon will have five sides, the fifth one labelled **R** representing the vector sum (the resultant) of the other four. The length and direction of **R** are found from a scale drawing or using trigonometry.

Note that (a) the directions of the four forces must follow round in the same direction. The sense of the resultant **R** is in the opposite direction.

(b) the forces may be added in any order i.e. the line segments may be drawn in any order.

(c) if the starting point A and the finishing point B happen to coincide, then $\mathbf{R} = \mathbf{0}$, i.e. the sum of the forces is zero.

This is not the most elegant method for adding more than two forces; it is more usual to write each force in components in two perpendicular directions, and then to add them.

See ***force***.

POTENTIAL ENERGY (PE) The energy a body has that is due to its position. It is the result of a conservative force and is the work done by that force in moving the body from its present position to the position of zero potential energy. The formula for PE depends on the force.

Gravitational Potential Energy

If the conservative force is gravity, there will be two different potential energies depending upon how the gravitational force is modelled; the usual model is to assume that the magnitude of the force of gravity is constant and equal to mg. In this case the potential energy is mgh where h is the vertical height of the centre of gravity of the body above the level of zero PE. Note that if the centre of gravity is below this level, then its potential energy is negative. The zero level of PE is often taken to be ground level, but in problems, the choice of the zero level is arbitrary. The other model is that the magnitude of the force of gravity is given by Newton's Law of Gravitation; so $|\mathbf{F}| = \frac{GMm}{r^2}$ and the potential energy is $-\frac{GMm}{r}$.

The first model is appropriate for distances close to the surface of the Earth. This is valid even at the top of Everest, 8.848 km above sea-level. The second model for gravity is necessary for objects in space, e.g. satellites.

Elastic Potential Energy

If the force is the tension in an elastic string of natural length ℓ and modulus of elasticity λ and if the force obeys Hooke's Law, then the PE of the stretched string is $\dfrac{\lambda x^2}{2\ell}$ where x is the extension.

The SI unit for potential energy is the joule (J).

POWER The rate at which work is done.

The SI unit of power is the watt and 1 watt = 1 joule/sec.

For a vehicle moving in a straight line, the power of the engine is the product $T \times v$ where T is the driving force and v the speed of the vehicle.

More generally, power may be written as the scalar product of the two vectors, force **F** and velocity **v**, thus the power of **F** is **F.v**.

PRESSURE The force exerted per unit area in the direction at right angles to the surface. The SI unit is the pascal i.e. 1 newton per square metre.

PRINCIPLE OF MOMENTS The sum of the moments of a set of coplanar forces about a point in the plane is equal to the moment of the resultant of the forces about the same point. This principle is used for finding the positions of centres of gravity.

R

RADIUS OF GYRATION (symbol k) See ***moment of inertia***.

RECTILINEAR MOTION Motion along a straight line.

RELATIVE VELOCITY If A and B are two bodies travelling with velocities $\mathbf{v}_A$ and $\mathbf{v}_B$ respectively, then the velocity of A relative to B is $(\mathbf{v}_A - \mathbf{v}_B)$.

For example, if the velocities of A and B are as shown in the table, then the relative velocities are as given:

	velocity of A	velocity of B	velocity of A relative to B
(1)	$60 \text{ m s}^{-1} \rightarrow$	$10 \text{ m s}^{-1} \rightarrow$	$50 \text{ m s}^{-1} \rightarrow$
(2)	$60 \text{ m s}^{-1} \rightarrow$	$10 \text{ m s}^{-1} \leftarrow$	$60 - (-10) = 70 \text{ m s}^{-1} \rightarrow$

In two dimensions (or more) it is more difficult to make sense of the answer. It helps to change the words 'relative to' to 'as it would appear to'. Thus in the second example, 70 m s^{-1} is the speed of A as it would appear to B. Consider the following situation with A and B travelling at right angles as shown below:

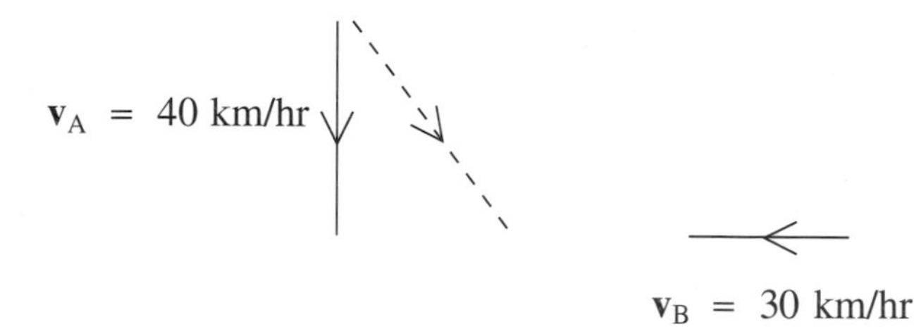

As seen by B, A would appear to be coming in a direction something like that indicated by the dotted line.

The velocity of A relative to B = $\mathbf{v}_A - \mathbf{v}_B = \mathbf{v}_A + (-\mathbf{v}_B)$

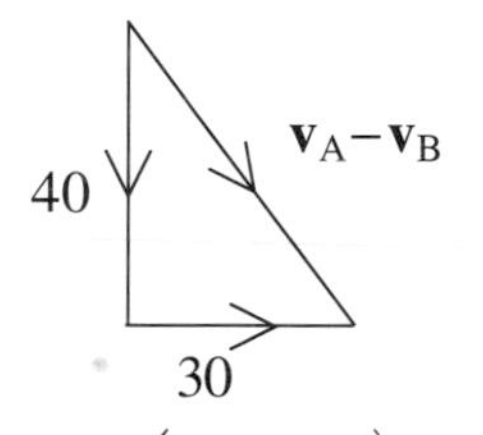

and the relative velocity $(\mathbf{v}_A - \mathbf{v}_B)$ is as expected and equal to 50 km/hr in the direction indicated in the diagram.

RESOLVE To find the components of a vector (e.g. a velocity, a force) usually in perpendicular directions. For example, we may choose to resolve a set of forces in the horizontal and vertical directions.

See also ***components of a force***.

RESTITUTION, COEFFICIENT OF (symbol e) A measure of the elasticity or 'bouncyness' of an impact when two objects collide and then separate. The value of e lies between 0 and 1.

For a perfectly inelastic collision, e.g. two lumps of putty colliding, e takes the value 0.

For a perfectly elastic impact, e.g. certain rubber balls, e takes the value 1 and no kinetic energy is lost in the impact.

See also ***Newton's Experimental Law***.

RESTITUTION, LAW OF Same as Newton's Experimental Law.

RESULTANT The sum of two or more vectors, e.g. the resultant of a set of forces is the vector sum of the forces, ie the single force that is equivalent to the original set of forces.

RETARDATION In common usage, this is a measure of how fast a speed is decreasing – the body in question is slowing down – and in elementary work this is often said to correspond to a negative acceleration. In fact this is not always true – it depends upon the direction which is defined as positive. For instance, consider a particle moving with Simple Harmonic Motion along the line AOB with O as the origin and OB the positive direction:–

A   O   B

when the particle travels from O to A, it is slowing down and yet the acceleration is positive; whereas from B to O, its speed is increasing and yet the acceleration is negative.

It is preferable to avoid the word 'retardation' altogether.

RIGID BODY An ideal body whose shape is not deformed no matter what forces are applied to it, i.e. the distance between any two particles of the body remains constant.

The body thus cannot be considered to be a single particle and forces may act at different points of the body. Both the position of a force and its magnitude will affect the resulting motion. Thus a rigid body will move as a result of two different types of motion :–

(1) the linear motion of its centre of mass.

(2) the rotational motion of the body about an axis (the axis need not be fixed).

The first is governed by Newton's Second Law $\mathbf{F} = m\mathbf{a}$:–

The sum of the external forces	=	*the rate of change of linear momentum.*

The second is governed by the rotational form of $\mathbf{F} = m\mathbf{a}$:–

The sum of the moments of the external forces about a point A	=	*the rate of change of angular momentum about* A.

where A is a fixed point or the centre of mass (which need not be fixed).

ROLLING CONDITION The relation between the linear and angular speeds of a sphere or cylinder which rolls without sliding.

If the speed of the centre is v and the angular speed is ω then the rolling condition is $v = r\omega$ (where r = CP).

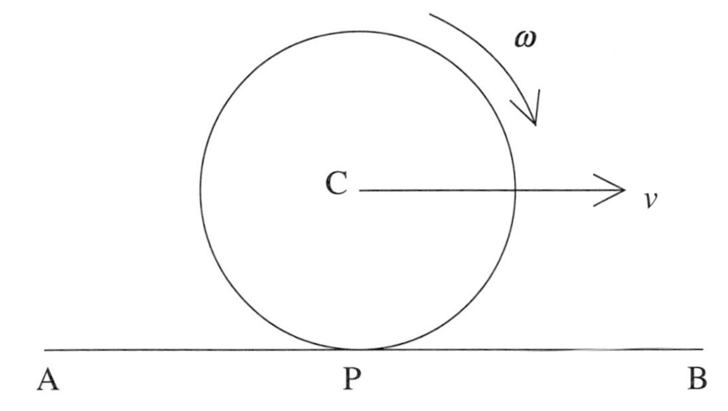

This condition can be shown as follows:

The velocity of P on the sphere (cylinder) relative to the centre C

$$= r\omega \text{ in the direction PA.}$$

Therefore the velocity of P relative to the ground AB

$$= (v - r\omega) \text{ in the direction PB.}$$

P is instantaneously at rest if there is rolling without sliding so

$$v - r\omega = 0$$

and $v = r\omega$ as required.

S

SCALAR PRODUCT For two vectors **a** and **b**, the scalar product is written **a.b** and defined by: $\mathbf{a.b} = ab \cos\theta$

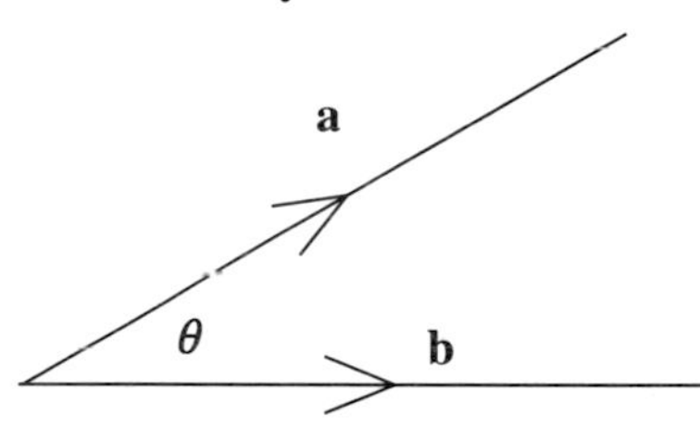

where θ is the angle between the vectors.

If $\mathbf{a} = a_1\mathbf{i} + a_2\mathbf{j} + a_3\mathbf{k}$ and $\mathbf{b} = b_1\mathbf{i} + b_2\mathbf{j} + b_3\mathbf{k}$ then

$$\mathbf{a.b} = a_1b_1 + a_2b_2 + a_3b_3$$

(since $\mathbf{i.i} = \mathbf{j.j} = \mathbf{k.k} = 1$ and $\mathbf{i.j} = \mathbf{i.k} = \mathbf{j.k} = 0$.)

Thus we have

$$\boxed{\mathbf{a.b} = ab\cos\theta = a_1b_1 + a_2b_2 + a_3b_3}$$

Algebra:-

$$\mathbf{a.a} = a^2 \qquad \mathbf{a.b} = \mathbf{b.a}$$
$$\mathbf{a.}(\lambda\mathbf{b}) = \lambda\mathbf{a.b} \qquad (\mathbf{a} + \mathbf{b})\mathbf{.c} = \mathbf{a.c} + \mathbf{b.c}$$

For two non-zero vectors $\mathbf{a.b} = 0$ if and only if **a** and **b** are perpendicular. This is the most important property about the scalar product in elementary mathematics.

SECOND (s)

The SI unit of time defined by the duration of 9 192 631 770 periods of the radiation corresponding to the transition between two hyperfine levels of the ground state of caesium-133 atom.

SIMPLE HARMONIC MOTION (SHM) If a particle P is moving in a straight line in such a manner that its acceleration is directed towards a fixed point O on the line and has magnitude proportional to the distance OP, then it is said to be moving with Simple Harmonic Motion. In symbols, we may write the above definition as

$$\text{acceleration} = \frac{d^2x}{dt^2} = -\omega^2 x$$

where ω is a constant and x is measured from O.

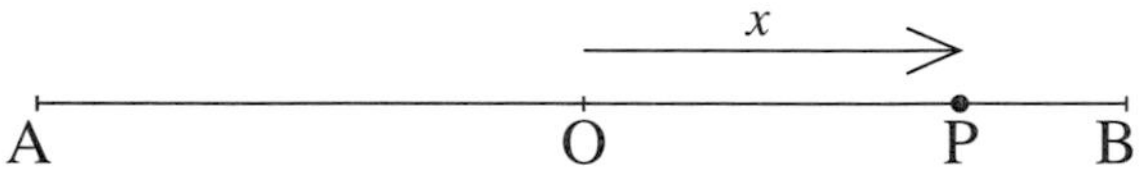

x →

A O P B

An equation of the form $\frac{d^2x}{dt^2} = -\omega^2 x$ or $\ddot{x} + \omega^2 x - 0$ is the standard form of the equation of motion for SHM. It can be shown that P oscillates along the line from A to B and back again. O is known as the centre of the motion and OA is the amplitude 'a'. The time taken to complete one oscillation, A to B to A, is called the period, T.

By integrating the equation $\ddot{x} = -\omega^2 x$, we obtain

(1) $v^2 = \omega^2 (a^2 - x^2)$

(2) $x = a \sin \omega t$ if $x = 0$ at $t = 0$

or $x = a \cos \omega t$ if $x = a$ when $t = 0$.

Or more generally, $x = A \cos \omega t + B \sin \omega t$ where A, B are the constants of integration.

(3) $T = \frac{2\pi}{\omega}$.

SIMPLE PENDULUM A heavy particle (the bob) attached to the end of a light string or light rod whose other end is fixed.

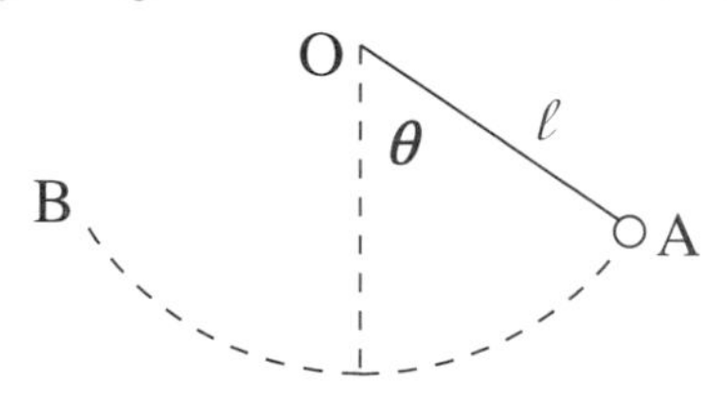

The bob oscillates from A to B and back, along the arc AB of the circle centre O.

If θ is small, it can be shown that the motion is approximately simple harmonic with period $2\pi\sqrt{\frac{\ell}{g}}$ where ℓ = OA.

SI UNITS The metric system of units adopted by international agreement in 1960. The letters SI stand for *Système International*.

There are seven base units (see Table 1) and two supplementary units (see Table 2) and a large number of derived units, 18 of which have special names:–

e.g.	*force*	newton	N	1 N = 1 kg ms^{-2}
	energy, work	joule	J	1 J = 1 N m
	power	watt	W	1 W = 1 N ms^{-1}

Table 1. Base units

Quantity	**Name of base SI unit**	**Symbol**
length	metre	m
mass	kilogram	kg
time	second	s
electric current	ampere	A
thermodynamic temperature	kelvin	K
amount of substance	mole	mol
luminous intensity	candela	cd

Table 2. Supplementary units

Quantity	Name of base SI unit	Symbol
plane angle	radian	rad
solid angle	steradian	sr

SMOOTH (mechanics) Frictionless.

In practice, friction is never zero but if the surface is smooth, the friction may be small enough, relative to the other forces, to be ignored.

SPECIAL RELATIVITY A theory which links the measurements of observers in different inertial frames. The speed of light c is assumed to have the same value for all observers.

Let two inertial frames S and S' have their x and x' axes, y and y' axes, and z and z' axes parallel and suppose the origin of S' moves with speed v along the x-axis of S. If their clocks show times t and t' respectively, then the coordinates are related by the Special Lorentz transformations

$$x' = \gamma(x - vt)$$

$$y' = y$$

$$z' = z$$

$$t' = \gamma\left(t - \frac{xv}{c^2}\right) \qquad \text{where } \gamma = \frac{1}{\sqrt{1 - \left(\frac{v}{c}\right)^2}}.$$

When $v << c$ these become the usual Galilean transformations $x' = x - vt, y' = y, z' = z$ and $t' = t$.

Physical laws must be covariant, that is, have the same form in all inertial frames.

Relativistic effects become apparent only when particle speed v is comparable with the speed of light c.

SPEED The rate of change of distance. Speed is a scalar quantity and is the name given to the magnitude of the velocity.

The SI units are m s^{-1}.

If the speed is constant, then speed $= \frac{\text{distance}}{\text{time}}$.

See also ***average speed***.

SPEED OF LIGHT (symbol c) In a vacuum, this is 299 792 458 m s^{-1} exactly. It is a fundamental constant.

SPEED-TIME GRAPH A graph that illustrates the speed of an object at various times. The y-axis is used for the speed which is, by definition, always positive (being the magnitude of the velocity vector). The path of the object may be curved or straight.

The gradient of the graph gives the rate of change of speed. Note that this is **not** the same as the acceleration of the object .

The area under the graph gives the distance travelled.

See also ***velocity-time graph, acceleration, retardation***.

STABLE EQUILIBRIUM A position of static equilibrium such that if the body is slightly moved, then it will, of its own accord, return to the equilibrium position.

See also ***neutral equilibrium, unstable equilibrium***.

STATIC EQUILIBRIUM See ***equilibrium***.

STRUT A rod in compression. The rod is usually part of a light framework of rods and its function is to prevent the framework from collapsing.

In problems involving light rods, it is usual to consider the equilibrium of the joints rather than the rods. So the forces on the joints at the ends of a strut AB below are in the directions given in the diagram:–

Note that the forces on the strut due to the joints are in opposite directions to the forces on the joints (by Newton's Third Law) as shown below:–

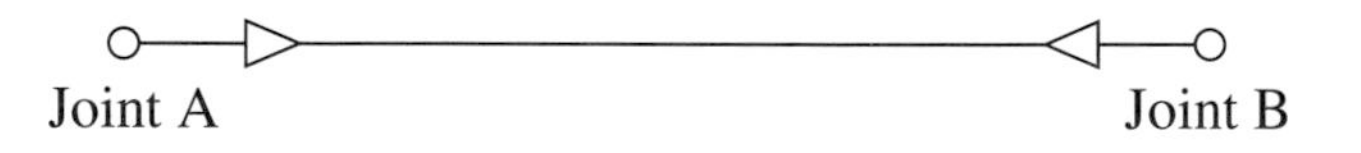

The force in a strut is often known as the thrust.

See also ***tie***.

T

TENSION The force in a string, spring or rod which is the result of it being pulled or stretched along its length.

THRUST The force in a strut. Any force that is pushing rather than pulling.

TIE A rod in tension. The rod is usually part of a light framework of rods and its function is to hold the framework together.

In problems involving light rods, it is usual to consider the equilibrium of the joints rather than the rods. So the forces on the joints at the ends of the tie *AB* below are in the directions given in the diagram:–

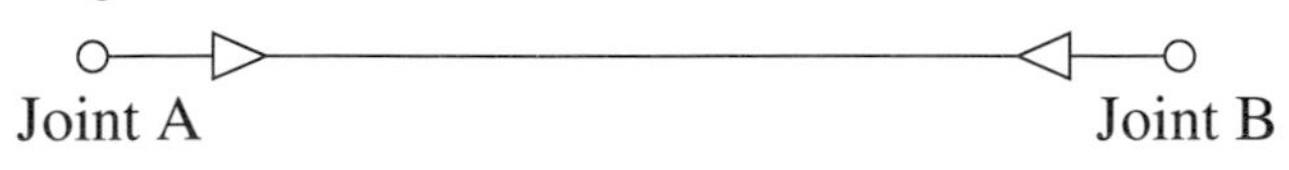

Note that the forces on the tie due to the joints are in the opposite directions (by Newton's Third Law) as shown below:–

The force in a tie is usually known as the tension.

See also ***strut***.

TIED VECTOR See ***localized vector***.

TONNE One thousand kilograms, formerly called the metric ton.

TORQUE Same as the moment of a force, or the moment of a couple.

TRIANGLE OF FORCES If two forces are represented in magnitude and direction by the sides *AB* and *BC* of a triangle, then the third side represents the sum, or resultant, of these forces

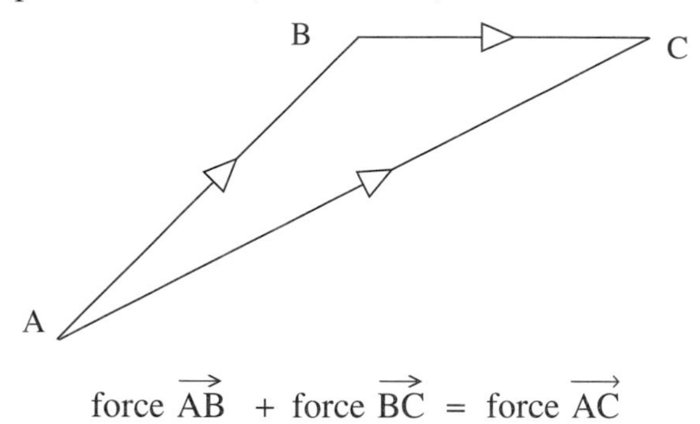

See also ***parallelogram of forces, polygon of forces***.

U

UNIFORM ACCELERATION Constant acceleration.

The magnitude and direction of the acceleration are fixed; e.g. the acceleration due to gravity.

UNIFORM BODY A body whose mass is distributed evenly throughout its volume. The importance of this in mechanics is that the centre of mass is at the centroid, i.e. the geometric centre of the body.

UNIFORM CIRCULAR MOTION Motion in a circle with constant speed.

UNIFORM SPEED Constant speed.

UNIFORM VELOCITY Constant velocity.

The speed and direction are fixed, so that there is no acceleration.

UNIVERSAL GRAVITATIONAL CONSTANT (G) The constant which appears in Newton's Law of Gravitation. $G = 6{\cdot}672 \times 10^{-11}\ \mathrm{Nm^2\ kg^{-2}}$.

UNSTABLE EQUILIBRIUM A position of static equilibrium such that if the body is slightly moved, then it will continue to move away from its original equilibrium position, i.e. it is no longer in equilibrium. Compare this with a position of stable equilibrium where the body, if moved slightly, will return to its equilibrium position.

See ***stable equilibrium, neutral equilibrium***.

V

VECTOR A quantity which has magnitude and direction, and which is added to another vector according to the triangle law of addition; thus if the vectors **a** and **b** are as shown

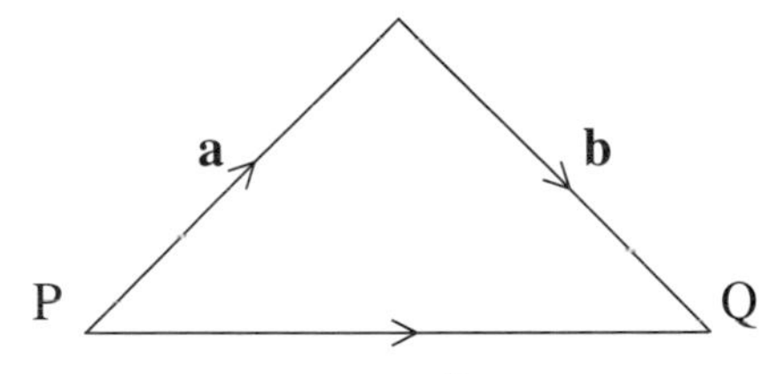

then the directed line segment $\overrightarrow{PQ}$ represents the sum of **a** and **b**.

We write $\overrightarrow{PQ} = \mathbf{a} + \mathbf{b}$.

Note that the position of the vector is not a part of the definition. Two vectors are equal if they have the same magnitude and direction wherever they are.

A particular vector may be written as a column matrix or in terms of unit vectors **i** and **j** in the *x* and *y* directions respectively, e.g.

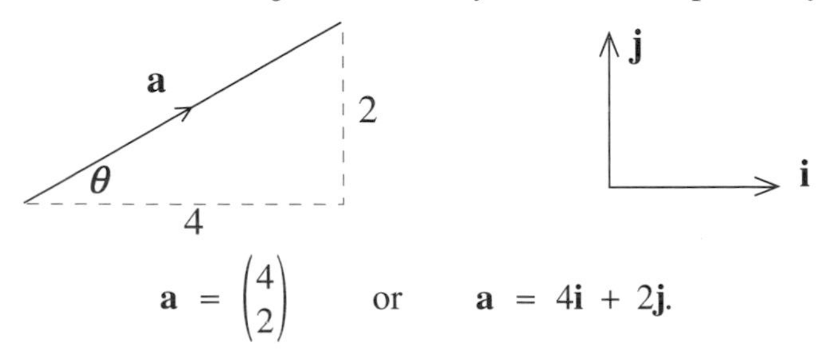

$$\mathbf{a} = \begin{pmatrix} 4 \\ 2 \end{pmatrix} \quad \text{or} \quad \mathbf{a} = 4\mathbf{i} + 2\mathbf{j}.$$

If a vector $\mathbf{b} = b_1\mathbf{i} + b_2\mathbf{j}$, then the magnitude of $\mathbf{b}$ is given by $|\mathbf{b}|$ or b where $b = \sqrt{b_1^2 + b_2^2}$.

The direction of $\mathbf{b}$ is given by the angle θ that it makes with the positive x-direction:– $\theta = \tan^{-1}\left(\frac{b_2}{b_1}\right)$.

The vector $\mathbf{r}$ usually denotes the position vector of a point relative to the origin. If the point P has coordinates (x, y)

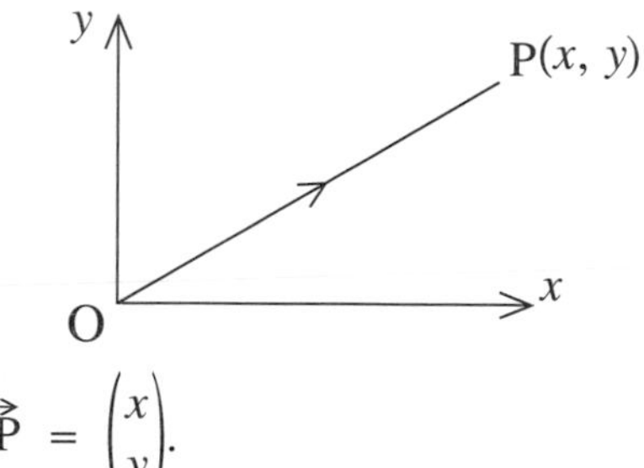

then $\mathbf{r} = \overrightarrow{OP} = \begin{pmatrix} x \\ y \end{pmatrix}$.

This is an example of a 'localized' vector where the starting point O is important. For 'free' vectors as defined above, the starting point is irrelevant.

The above examples are two-dimensional. It is a simple matter to extend them to three dimensions:

Thus the vector $\mathbf{a}$ may be $\begin{pmatrix} 4 \\ 2 \\ 3 \end{pmatrix}$ or $\mathbf{a} = 4\mathbf{i} + 2\mathbf{j} + 3\mathbf{k}$.

If point P has coordinates (x, y, z) then $\mathbf{r} = \overrightarrow{OP} = x\mathbf{i} + y\mathbf{j} + z\mathbf{k}$.

If vector $\mathbf{b} = b_1\mathbf{i} + b_2\mathbf{j} + b_3\mathbf{k}$ then $|\mathbf{b}| = b = \sqrt{b_1^2 + b_2^2 + b_3^2}$.

The direction of $\mathbf{b}$ cannot be so easily given as an angle with a certain line. Instead, we describe the direction by the direction ratios $b_1 : b_2 : b_3$.

See ***triangle of forces***.

VECTOR PRODUCT For two vectors **a** and **b** the vector product is written as $\mathbf{a} \times \mathbf{b}$ and defined by

$$\mathbf{a} \times \mathbf{b} = ab \sin\theta\, \hat{\mathbf{n}}$$

where $\hat{\mathbf{n}}$ is the unit vector at right angles to both **a** and **b**, and is in the sense shown in the diagram below. θ is the angle between the vectors.

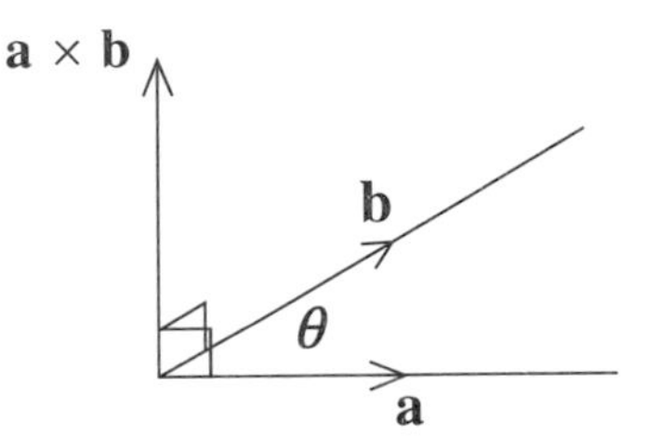

The direction of the vector product is determined by how a right-handed screw would move in turning from vector **a** to vector **b**; this rule is known as the "right-hand screw rule". Another description of this rule is:– looking in the direction of $\mathbf{a} \times \mathbf{b}$ through the plane of the vectors **a** and **b**, turning from **a** to **b** is a clockwise rotation through the angle θ.

Note that $\mathbf{b} \times \mathbf{a}$ would have the same magnitude but the opposite direction using the right-hand screw rule; thus $\mathbf{b} \times \mathbf{a} = -\mathbf{a} \times \mathbf{b}$ and so the vector product is not commutative.

If $\mathbf{a} = a_1\mathbf{i} + a_2\mathbf{j} + a_3\mathbf{k}$ and $\mathbf{b} = b_1\mathbf{i} + b_2\mathbf{j} + b_3\mathbf{k}$ then

$$\begin{aligned} \mathbf{a} \times \mathbf{b} &= (a_1\mathbf{i} + a_2\mathbf{j} + a_3\mathbf{k}) \times (b_1\mathbf{i} + b_2\mathbf{j} + b_3\mathbf{k}) \\ &= (a_2b_3 - a_3b_2)\mathbf{i} - (a_1b_3 - a_3b_1)\mathbf{j} + (a_1b_2 - a_2b_1)\mathbf{k} \end{aligned}$$

(since $\mathbf{i} \times \mathbf{j} = \mathbf{k} = -\mathbf{j} \times \mathbf{i}$, $\mathbf{j} \times \mathbf{k} = \mathbf{i} = -\mathbf{k} \times \mathbf{j}$, $\mathbf{k} \times \mathbf{i} = \mathbf{j} = -\mathbf{i} \times \mathbf{k}$ and $\mathbf{i} \times \mathbf{i} = \mathbf{j} \times \mathbf{j} = \mathbf{k} \times \mathbf{k} = \mathbf{0}$).

This is often written in determinant form, thus

$$\mathbf{a} \times \mathbf{b} = ab \sin\theta\, \hat{\mathbf{n}} = \begin{vmatrix} \mathbf{i} & a_1 & b_1 \\ \mathbf{j} & a_2 & b_2 \\ \mathbf{k} & a_3 & b_3 \end{vmatrix}$$

Algebra:– $\mathbf{a} \times \mathbf{a} = \mathbf{0}$, $\mathbf{a} \times \mathbf{b} = -\mathbf{b} \times \mathbf{a}$,

$\mathbf{a} \times \lambda\mathbf{b} = \lambda\mathbf{a} \times \mathbf{b}$, $(\mathbf{a} + \mathbf{b}) \times \mathbf{c} = \mathbf{a} \times \mathbf{c} + \mathbf{b} \times \mathbf{c}$

VELOCITY A vector quantity whose magnitude is the speed and whose direction is the direction of motion. It is precisely defined as the rate of change of displacement,

$$\text{i.e. } \mathbf{v} = \frac{d\mathbf{r}}{dt}. \quad \text{The SI unit is m s}^{-1}.$$

If a particle has position vectors $\mathbf{r}_1$ and $\mathbf{r}_2$ at the beginning and end of the time period t being considered, then the

$$\text{average velocity} = \frac{\mathbf{r}_2 - \mathbf{r}_1}{t}.$$

The velocity of a particle moving in a circle with radius r has magnitude $v = r\omega$.

The velocity of a particle moving in a plane, whose polar coordinates are (r, θ), is given by

$$\dot{\mathbf{r}} = \dot{r}\hat{\mathbf{r}} + r\dot{\theta}\hat{\boldsymbol{\theta}}$$

where $\hat{\mathbf{r}}$ is the unit vector parallel to the position vector and $\hat{\boldsymbol{\theta}}$ is the unit vector perpendicular to $\mathbf{r}$ in the direction of increasing θ.

VELOCITY-TIME GRAPH A graph that illustrates the velocity of a particle or object which is travelling in a straight line at various times.

The x-axis is used for the time measurements.

The gradient of the graph gives the acceleration of the particle.

The area under the graph gives the displacement.

These graphs are sometimes known as speed-time graphs; they are the same only if the velocity is positive for all values of t.

VIRTUAL FORCE The same as an inertial force.

See ***centrifugal force***.

W

WATT (*W*) The SI unit of power equal to 1 joule/sec. It is named after the Scottish engineer James Watt (1736 - 1789).

WEIGHT See ***mass and weight***.

WORK Considering the simplest case first, suppose a constant force of magnitude F acts on a body which causes it to move from A to B as shown

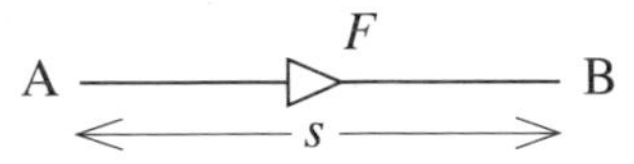

The work done by the force is defined to be 'force times distance'

$$= F \times s.$$

Work is a scalar quantity; the SI unit is the joule (J).

If now, $\mathbf{F}$ is at an angle θ to AB as shown below:

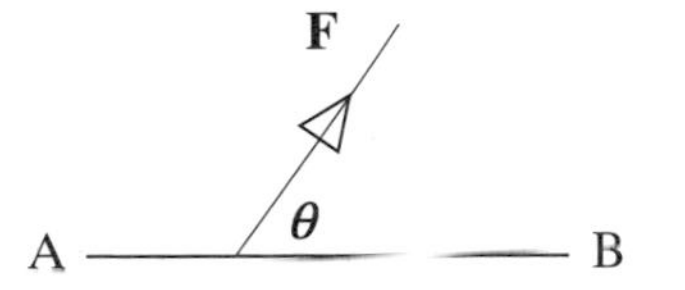

The work done by $\mathbf{F}$ is the work done by the component of $\mathbf{F}$ in the direction of AB (the component of $\mathbf{F}$ perpendicular to AB does no work on the body in moving it from A to B).

This is equal to $F \cos\theta \times s = \mathbf{F}.\,\overrightarrow{AB}$ (the scalar product).

More generally, suppose a variable force **F** acts on a particle as it moves along a curve from point A $(\mathbf{r}_0)$ to point B $(\mathbf{r}_1)$.

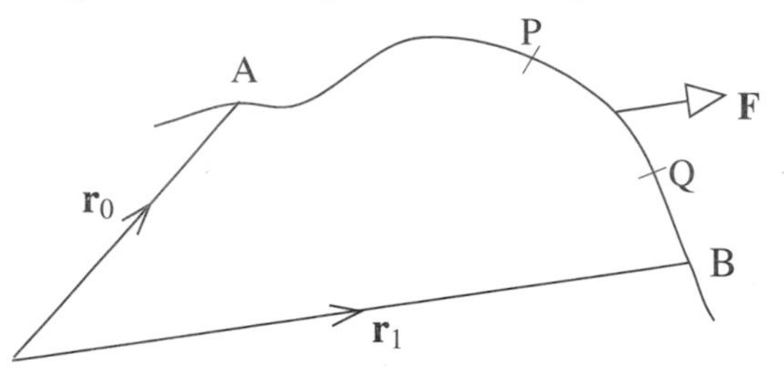

Then the work done by **F** over a small element PQ of the curve is approximately $\mathbf{F}.d\mathbf{r}$ (where $\overrightarrow{PQ} = d\mathbf{r}$).

The total work done by **F** as the particle moves from A to B along the curve is the line integral $\int_{\mathbf{r}_0}^{\mathbf{r}_1} \mathbf{F}.d\mathbf{r}$.

In general, its value depends upon the shape of the curve connecting A and B.

WORK-ENERGY EQUATION

The equation 'work done = increase in KE'.

This equation arises when Newton's Second Law is integrated. In the following, it must be remembered that the 'F' or '$\mathbf{F}$' in Newton's Second Law signifies the sum of all the forces.

In one dimension, we write the acceleration $\dfrac{dv}{dt}$ as $v\dfrac{dv}{dx}$ and integrate both sides with respect to x:

$$F = mv\,\frac{dv}{dx}$$

$$\int_0^x F\,dx = \int_u^v mv\,dv = \frac{mv^2}{2} - \frac{mu^2}{2}$$

[or if the force is constant, $Fx = \dfrac{mv^2}{2} - \dfrac{mu^2}{2}$]

i.e. $\quad$ *work done by the forces* = *final KE* − *initial KE*

or $\quad$ *work done* = *increase in KE.*

In more than one dimension, the mathematics is slightly more sophisticated: start from Newton's Second Law in the form $\mathbf{F} = m\ddot{\mathbf{r}}$ and form the scalar product with the velocity $\dot{\mathbf{r}}$ and then integrate both sides with respect to time. Thus

$$\mathbf{F}.\dot{\mathbf{r}} = m\ddot{\mathbf{r}}.\dot{\mathbf{r}}$$

$$\int_0^t \mathbf{F}.\dot{\mathbf{r}}\,dt = \int_0^t m\ddot{\mathbf{r}}.\dot{\mathbf{r}}\,dt = \left[\tfrac{1}{2}m\dot{\mathbf{r}}^2\right]_0^t$$

$$= \tfrac{1}{2}mv^2 - \tfrac{1}{2}mu^2.$$

$$\text{LHS} = \int_0^t \mathbf{F}.\dot{\mathbf{r}}\,dt = \int \mathbf{F}.\frac{d\mathbf{r}}{dt}\,dt = \int \mathbf{F}.d\mathbf{r} = \textit{work done by forces.}$$

Hence again we obtain the work-energy equation

work done = *increase in KE.*